5 ELEMENT
Alchemy

5 ELEMENT
Alchemy

USE YOUR 5 ELEMENT TYPE TO EMBRACE YOUR GIFTS & CREATE A LIFE YOU LOVE

ASHLEY ABBS

EMBODIED ELEMENTS PRESS

Publisher: Embodied Elements Press
Editor: Kathryn Willms of Kwill Communications
Front cover image: Talonx.com
Front cover design: Angela Hammersmith

Issued in print and electronic formats.
ISBN 978-1-7775456-0-4 (paperback).-- 978-1-7775456-1-1 (EPUB). 978-1-7775456-2-8 (MOBI)

This is an original print edition of *5 Element Alchemy*.

For Sheldon and Elijah

Healing may not be so much about getting better as about letting go of everything that isn't you, all of the expectations, all of the beliefs – and becoming who you are.

– Rachel Naomi Remen

Contents

Part 1

5 Element Alchemy: Why You Are the Way You Are

Part 2

Put Your Alchemy into Practice: Create a Life You Love

Part 1

5 Element Alchemy:
Why You Are the Way You Are

Chapter 1

Discover Your 5 Element Alchemy

Welcome to 5 Element Alchemy

Before you read any further, you need to know something important. Right now, without having done a single exercise in this book, you are enough, you are worthy, you are safe, you are powerful, and you are loved. You are whole, just as you are. You might be shaking your head in disagreement. This might not feel true. Many of us have a recording in our heads that plays on a loop and tells us differently, but that inner monologue doesn't change what's inherently true. You already have the answers you seek. You need only to recognize them.

This book is meant to provide you medicine to help guide and support you to remember your inherent gifts and answer the questions you have about why you are the way you are. You will be given the means to unapologetically embrace all parts of yourself – even those you feel you need to fix or hide from everyone, maybe even yourself. If you're looking for permission to live and create a life of your own design, here it is. I am not granting it; you are. The 5 Elements and your Alchemy will help show you the way. Let's get started.

Why the 5 Elements?

5 Element theory, which comes from Chinese medicine, is intricate and steeped in tradition; however, there is also a simplicity to it. For many, it feels organic.

For me, that was certainly true. The 5 Elements provided an entry point to a deeper understanding of myself, confirming who I am as a person, why I behave the way I do, how I assert myself, and why and how I seek comfort. The 5 Elements allowed me to relax and trust myself and my intuition, while also cultivating supports for my deficiencies so that I may utilize and embody each Element and its medicine to fully express the person that I am meant to be and create a life that I love. I hope you too find that the 5 Elements guide you home to your soul and your deep inner knowing.

In this first half of the book, you will identify your Element type. This will allow you to celebrate all the unique quirks and tendencies that you possess while identifying behaviors and mindsets that might cause you to struggle. A deeper examination of each Element will support you in breaking negative habits and creating nurturing practices that will help you foster supportive relationships, develop greater ease with your body, and improve how you connect with your work. In the second half of the book, you will apply this knowledge to different areas of life. Through this process, the steady steps that will guide you to create a life that you truly love will reveal themselves. What you will not find is a 10-point, one-size-fits-all checklist. This medicine is about understanding and being true to your soul. Every person's Alchemy and path are unique; you will curate a life of your own choosing and making.

I'll be honest: there are places in this book that get a bit heavy. Nothing will be revealed that you probably don't already know, but there may be some things that you've buried, unsure of how to deal with them. As you begin this process of honoring your whole self using the language and wisdom of the 5 Elements, you will find that moments of reflection and insight will initiate a desire to tend to yourself or heal so that you may evolve into the next level of YOU.

Trust that holding space for what surfaces will in fact begin the healing process. There is medicine here. The 5 Elements will offer solutions to shift your energy and find a sense of peace. Not only that but through the framework of the 5 Elements and Chinese medicine, your true nature will surface, and you will begin to cultivate an ability to hold all sides of a situation. What you may have previously considered to be "good" or "bad" can be transformed with a new level of acceptance and compassion to be embraced as simply what is. And, with this lens, you will find you have the tools available to approach life in a new light.

A Brief History

The idea that all of nature is governed by yin, yang and the 5 Elements lies at the heart of Chinese medicine as it was laid down over 2000 years ago. The *Neijing*, or the *Yellow Emperor's Classic of Medicine*, written in 200 BC, explained how the natural forces of yin and yang, Qi, and the 5 Elements (defined as Earth, Metal, Water, Wood, and Fire) could be understood and utilized to achieve balance and harmony in life. It also described how the human body experiences disease through the natural aging process and the environment. It is considered one of the most important written works of traditional Chinese medicine (TCM) and still informs how practitioners practice today. In the era that it was written, there was little distinction made between religion, philosophy, science and medicine, which allowed the concepts and theory of Chinese medicine to be infused with ideas from Daoism, Naturalism, Confucianism, along with other branches of religious and philosophical thought.[1]

The principles of yin and yang as described in the *Neijing* are the cornerstone of all theories of Chinese medicine, informing us of the concept of dualism, where two opposing energetics are complementary, inseparable and interdependent. Light does not exist without dark, feminine without masculine, or cold without heat. Acknowledging one of these requires us to consider its opposite, which provides us with an opportunity to examine everything in relationship. If there is a deficiency in yin, there is likely to be an excess of yang.

Yin and yang give rise to an even more nuanced relationship known as Wu Xing, which is the belief that all energy in the world can be divided

---

[1] Hicks, A., Hicks, J., & Mole, P. (2011). *Five element constitutional acupuncture*. Churchill Livingstone.

into five movements or processes, which are also referred to as phases or elements. For simplicity, we'll use the term "Element" to refer to these five fundamental qualities of all matter in the universe – Earth, Metal, Water, Wood, and Fire. Each of these Elements form a relationship with yin and yang, where some are considered more yin and others more yang. There is also a microcosm of the yin/yang relationship occurring within each of the Elements themselves. Through the lens of the Elements, practitioners and individuals alike come to view everything from the environment to themselves as wholes. And they can see how the Elements, with their complex dynamics and differing points of perspective, come into right relationship with each other. Throughout this book, I will return to this idea of "right relationship." When something is in right relationship, it has agency but is still interconnected to the whole.[2]

Within the theory and practice of the 5 Elements, each Element has a particular set of associations, such as a yin and a yang organ, color, sound, and season, among other characteristics. And each Element governs a part of the whole; for example, the energetic of the Wood Element governs the season of spring, which has its own characteristics and energetics. We are better able to identify these, and their unique characteristics and medicine, when we see them in relationship to the other Elements or seasons. Together they provide a well-rounded look at everything from our health to our natural tendencies, to why we make the decisions we do individually and in relationship to our environment and other people.

Each of us embodies all 5 Elements, and different Elements will become more pronounced to support us through the changes that occur in our lives. However, it is believed that all of us are born with one constitutional Element that is more dominant than the others. This plays a pivotal part in the early development of repetitive patterns, thoughts, and emotions, as well as a yearning for particular requirements to be met as we move through the world and our life experiences.

---

[2] Maciocia, G. (1989). *The foundations of Chinese medicine.* Churchill Livingstone.

Acupuncturists in ancient times discovered they could look at the imbalances and strengths in individuals to determine a person's main Elemental nature and personality. Equipped with this knowledge, patients could achieve greater health by holding space for both the person they currently were as well as the evolutionary path that would lead to their growth and development.

Today, practitioners still use the 5 Elements to diagnose and support their patients; however, much of what is taught in the West is devoid of the brilliance of the original teachings. This is because when traditional Chinese medicine was brought over and marketed to the West during the Cultural Revolution in China in the '60s and '70s under the communist regime, anything related to the spirit or religion was left out to ensure that the medicine was aligned with the principles of rationalism and atheism.[3] Focused more on acupuncture and herbalism, the 5 Elements became a lesser-known theory than other forms of thought and philosophy that included the idea of Elements, most of which were birthed in the West by the Greeks and cited in astrology alongside pagan rituals and traditions.

As a result, those of us who wish to hold space for spirit, psychology and Alchemy in our practices must dig deeper, returning to the classics of our medicine and seeking mentors who follow the lineage of teachers who helped to sustain and protect this medicine over the centuries, notably several acupuncturists in Europe who date back to the 1920s such as George Soulié de Morant, Jacques-André Lavier and later J.R. Worsley, a British osteopath who is credited with bringing the 5 Elements to the West in the 1970s.[4] As more ancient texts are translated by scholars, this is becoming even more possible. This influx of knowledge has allowed us practitioners to better transmit the impact of this medicine to our patients to aid in their transformation and healing.

---

[3] Kaptchuk, T. (2000). *The web that has no weaver.* Contemporary Publishing Group.

[4] Kirkwood, J. (2016). *The way of the five elements.* Singing Dragon.

Embodying the Medicine

The 5 Elements is a system based on wholes, from the microcosm of an individual to the macrocosm of our planet earth and our universe. It does not only provide information about our inner psyches, it also supports us in the wider world, acting as a rich and valuable reference point. You can access this medicine at every turn and season. Just by going out your front door, putting your feet in the dirt, and breathing in the fresh air.

When people initially learn about the 5 Elements, they seem like a foreign language or a mystical religion. What's funny is they're the opposite: you may have not been aware of them, but you have a relationship with them right now. So instead of introducing you to the 5 Elements, I'm going to reacquaint you with them and their medicine.

That tendency to slow down and yearn to be cozy, watching Netflix in your pajamas, on a cold and rainy/snowy day? That is one aspect of Water.

Feel empowered when spring emerges? Suddenly, you feel awake and ready to tackle a new project. This is the Wood Element wanting to drive upward and onward, projecting itself into the future.

Does the heat of summer cause you to lose some of your inhibition, fall in love, connect with friends, and maybe even crave community? The Fire Element invites us to enjoy the warmth and excites the spirit, allowing us to feel a little more extroverted.

Like I said, you inherently know these Elements. We're just going to get more familiar with their language and be intentional about connecting the dots so you can choose to engage with them, recognize your relationship to them, and ultimately, cultivate them to support your life and greater desires.

My favorite part of this medicine, and why I love sharing it with others, is that it can be accessed so easily. You can see the Elements thriving in our environment, in the changing of the seasons and the phases of the moon. They are even reflected within our bodies, through a woman's menstrual cycle and pregnancy, and all our different phases of life. As disparate as these things may seem, they are all influenced by the cycling of the Elements from one to the other, and when you can bring your attention to how these Elements show up for you, within you, and around you, you can choose to tap into this potential whenever you want. Each time you do this, your next step becomes available – and it feels steady, aligned and right for you and what you need in that moment.

But it's a choice.

A choice that requires us to be open to thinking about the ways we interact with our environment and the people we love. The 5 Elements are cyclical; together, they form a whole system that leads from one Element to the next, coming full circle only to repeat over and over again. These transitions between Elements provide opportunities for growth, with each Element offering a different perspective and energetic to inform our decisions and mindset. Becoming aware of these cycles, we can reflect, integrate and revisit situations, beliefs and relationships both with greater understanding of ourselves and a thread of momentum that facilitates our transformation.

The 5 Elements don't have the polarities that our culture has conditioned us to abide by. It's important to notice the tendency we have to approach everything as a duality: this/that, left/right, right/wrong, good/bad, even yin/yang. But of course, as yin/yang reminds us, these are interdependent and in constant relationship with one another. Even in the depths of the most yin, there is still yang, and vice versa. Remembering this allows us to hold space for the moments of gray, the space in between the absolutes, where we live most of our lives.

Throughout this book you will be invited to suspend your desire or need to proclaim that there is only one answer or way of doing something. The 5 Elements are not fixed, and they are certainly not linear; they move. Through their movement they provide information and medicine. Understanding how your own relationship to the Elements changes can bring fresh insights and lead you to greater depths of understanding of yourself and your potential.

I invite you to trust the wisdom of the 5 Elements. They seek to bring everything together to produce harmony and wholeness. They can help reveal the wholeness within you too. While the 5 Elements can serve us in a multitude of contexts, we will be focusing on how they can be used as a personality system to support a greater understanding of why you are the way you are. We will also be examining how the Elements govern the inner workings of your everyday life, to explain why you may feel ease in one area and completely lost in another. This knowledge culminates to support you in creating a life in alignment with your soul and inspired by love.

The Elements Manifested in Nature

Before we discuss the Elements as they manifest in you individually, it is helpful to connect with their energetics as you experience them in nature. Becoming aware of what imagery and sensory feelings they inspire can deepen your understanding of them as a whole but also how you relate to each of them.

Let's start with the Water Element. Water can be still and clear. It ebbs and flows, but it can also be turbid and rough. It can trickle like a stream or come in like a powerful tidal wave. A single rainfall can cause a seed to sprout or a tsunami of destruction. Water goes with the flow, but enough water flowing over time can erode mountains. In any of these forms, it acts as a catalyst, making things happen. Water's season is winter. Your associations with this season may be different depending on where you live. In my home in Calgary, Canada, winter means snow, and it can be brutally cold at times, perpetuating an invitation to slow down and go inward to reflect and listen.

The Wood Element. The sprout breaks through the soil and becomes a tree that grows upward to the light. Trees have direction. They are strong and well rooted while remaining flexible to weather a storm. Wood's season is spring, when there's a bustling of yang energy. Here, we feel empowered to clear and clean up our path so we can forge ahead, acting with an assertive nature to accomplish our mandate.

The Fire Element has many forms: a spark, ash, smoke, embers, a full-out blaze. Much like Water, Fire is a catalyst that can cause a flurry of activity. It can be set intentionally to renew the soil in a field and cultivate a new crop. Or it can be set recklessly or accidentally, burning up everything in its path, leaving nothing, never looking back. Its season is summer, when it's usually hot, allowing us to be out and about, connecting, collaborating, celebrating, falling in love.

The Earth Element. Mother Earth, need I say more? Fertility, dirt, and soil, the Earth Element governs the harvest and its bounty. It represents abundance, the mother with her unconditional love. The Earth Element has no specific season, although some associate it with late summer (because of the harvest). It holds the transitions between the seasons, acting as the center and the connection, always there. Like a mother, its work is never done.

The last of the Elements is Metal. It is also associated with ore, rock, and precious stones. At first, we may think of metal as being hard, rigid and structured, but we must remember that metals can be melted down, rock can be chiseled, clay can be molded. Metal can be altered and created into something new. Metal invites us to evoke the artist within, allowing for the capacity to refine, transform and create anew. Its season is autumn, in which we pivot back to the self. Like the leaves that turn to golds and browns before letting go, the energetic of Metal supports us to let go of patterns and beliefs that we no longer need, thus giving us the opportunity to begin anew.

My hope is that these associations have helped to create some form of felt sense and remembering of the Elements and will inform the lens through which you interpret this medicine. Each person will experience these Elements and their manifestations differently, in part due to geography but more importantly because of your individual Alchemy.

Discover Your Alchemy: Take the 5 Element Quiz

Before we go any further, it's important for you to identify your 5 Element type by taking this short quiz. DON'T OVERTHINK THIS! This is not like your SATs or any other exams you have taken in your life. Keep it simple: give the first answer that comes to mind. If you think that there are two possible answers, go with the one that feels truer to you in this moment. We are not looking for what the answer would be if you were your best self, or what you think the most enlightened answer would be. You can't get this wrong; no Element type is better than another. Let's do this.

1. What color are you most drawn to?
a) Dark Blue
b) Green
c) Red
d) Earth Tones (Browns and Golds)
e) White

2. What's your favorite season?
a) Winter
b) Spring
c) Summer
d) Late Summer or Harvest Season
e) Autumn

3. What time of day are you at your best?
a) Afternoon
b) Late Night
c) Midday and Dusk
d) Morning
e) Sunrise

4. What are your innate gifts?
a) Wisdom and Insight
b) Confidence and Assertiveness
c) Communication
d) Nurture and Support
e) Organization

5. What reaction are you prone to during troubling times?

a) Suspicion

b) Depression

c) Restless Sleep or Hypersensitivity

d) Anxiety or Worry

e) Rigidity or Inflexibility

6. What does your voice sound like?

a) Quiet or Moaning

b) Shouting

c) Fast Chatter

d) Singing and Melodic

e) Clear with a Slight Tremble

7. What inspires you?

a) Philosophical Discussion

b) Making Things Happen

c) Creating Community and Intimacy

d) Creating Harmony in Everything

e) Art and Creativity

8. How do you relax?

a) Reading

b) Watching TV

c) Dancing

d) Hanging Out with Friends

e) Projects (Arts and Crafts, etc.)

9. What's your strongest mental ability?

a) Big Picture Thinking and Risk Assessment

b) Vision and Drive

c) Openness

d) Being Present

e) Being Disciplined

10. To which physical weaknesses are you prone?

a) Spine, Urination, Sexual

b) Headaches, Blood Pressure

c) Heart Palpitations, Insomnia

d) Weight Gain, Sluggishness

e) Breathing, Skin Problems

11. What is your emotional tendency when feeling overwhelmed?

a) Isolation

b) Rage

c) Becoming Excitable, Forgetful

d) Seeking Comfort

e) Being Hypercritical or Sad

12. Do you like new things or change?

a) Sure

b) Of Course

c) Always

d) Not Really

e) No

13. Do you like to socialize?

a) Rarely

b) Oh Yeah!

c) Always

d) With a Few Friends

e) Selectively

14. How do you express yourself when interacting with others?

a) Honest

b) Intense

c) Enthusiastic

d) Sympathetic

e) Direct; To the Point

15. How would people who know you describe you?

a) Unusual and a Dreamer

b) Ambitious and Competitive

c) Attractive and Magnetic

d) Loyal and Accessible

e) Classy and Discriminating

16. What are your preferences for group work and projects?

a) To Work Alone

b) To Be the Lead

c) To Collaborate

d) To Create Harmony within the Group

e) To Ensure Everyone Understands Their Objective

17. What is your ideal way to move your body?

a) Yoga

b) Something That Pushes Me to My Limits

c) Dancing

d) Anything with Friends

e) Running by Yourself

18. What would your ideal vacation be?

a) A Retreat for Self-Work

b) Something Adventurous

c) The Beach

d) Family Trip

e) Museums and Architecture

19. What feeling is most dominant in you?

a) Fear

b) Frustration

c) Elation

d) Worry

e) Sadness

20. What quality do you value most in yourself?
a) Insight
b) Power
c) Compassion
d) Nurturing
e) Meticulousness

21. Which quality do you value most in others?
a) Depth
b) Confidence
c) Vulnerability
d) Honor
e) Self-Control

22. What gives you the most difficulty?
a) Authority
b) Indecision
c) Boundaries
d) Saying No
e) Spontaneity

23. Which quality of yours do friends and family have difficulty with?
a) Elusiveness
b) Bossiness
c) Being Clingy or Overemotional
d) Being Wishy-Washy
e) Rigidity

24. What qualities help you in your vocation?
a) Independence
b) Leadership
c) Star Power
d) Dependability
e) Discipline

25. What are your dominant qualities?

a) Intelligent - Insightful

b) Powerful - Born Leader

c) Talkative - Joyful

d) Empathetic - Stable

e) Fastidious – Organized

Add up the number of a, b, c, d, and e's that you answered. The answers that have the highest score are your dominant Element(s).

a's ___2___ /25 Water

b's ___4___ /25 Wood

c's ___5___ /25 Fire

d's ___9___ /25 Earth

e's ___6___ /25 Metal

Write your numbers on the lines in the 5 Element Alchemy chart.

An Overview of 5 Element Alchemy

Now that you have your numbers, we can dig into what makes you YOU specifically. There are many things that create an identity. Some of these are contextual, such as your family history, geographic location, culture, etc. Others, such as your thoughts, emotions, actions, daily practices, habits, and gifts, are formed through the interplay of your context with your unique personality, being, and soul. 5 Element Alchemy can help you strip back the layers to uncover the true person inside. You are unique, incredible, and whole just as you are; now it's time to see that as the truth.

Every Element operates on a physical, mental and spiritual level. Once you know your dominant Element type, you can make choices to support its energetics to create the life you want. Being able to confirm and embody who you are is a liberating and powerful experience, allowing you to easily tap into your intuition to make decisions that support your core requirements, which we'll get to in a bit.

As you connect with your dominant Element, you may find that it does not fully encompass your personality or how you show up in the world. This is where your Alchemy comes in. Within each of us are ALL the Elements. We embody them at different seasons, in different times in our life, or when we need to in order to support our growth and development.

You may have one, two or even three secondary Elements that also influence the way you express yourself in your daily life. Even being deficient in an Element can hold answers for you. This is why I recommend that you read each Element type chapter. I don't blame you if you want to skip ahead to learn more about your dominant Element – I totally would! But I implore you to go back and read the rest, so that you can get a full picture of who you are, and possibly even learn something about the people in your life who identify with another Element type.

Let's now take a few moments to go over your chart as a whole before we get into the specifics. This will help you take in the detailed information in a more meaningful way. This information can also help you refine your daily practices and activities to better support you and avoid harmful patterns that will tip you even further off-balance and away from your soul's purpose.

Your Individual Alchemy: Why You Are the Way You Are

As I mentioned previously, we are surrounded by the 5 Elements and their cycles, but we also have the 5 Elements within us. However, how they show up for each of us is different. No two people's Alchemies are the same.

When you start working with the 5 Elements and your Alchemy chart, I find it best to first take a step back and look at everything as a whole.

Yes, you are an Earth or Wood or whatever your dominant Element is, but you also encompass all of them. You may have secondary Elements in the background, pulling your dominant Element to behave in a particular way. Some Elements may be nonexistent in your chart, which also impacts how you move through life. This is important to remember. Reading about your dominant and secondary Elements, you will find aspects that ring true, but you also have a relationship with the Elements that aren't showing up at all in your chart. In fact, you may find more insight in exploring these Elements. They might represent places where you feel really challenged or that you wish to avoid, but I bet medicine is waiting for you there.

So before you jump ahead, take a moment to look at your chart and notice:

Are you currently more yin (with dominance showing up in Earth, Metal or Water), or more yang (with dominance in Wood, Fire or Water)? Water holds space in both, as it can be still and receptive and/or a moving catalyst. Or perhaps you have a good balance?

If your chart is more yin, it's likely that you are more introverted than someone more yang dominant. Cool, calm and collected, you think before you do, and your actions may be more subtle, although not less impactful. You likely have a keen eye for the details, and because of that, a little goes a long way. Yin is less showy, usually unseen, welcoming you into the depths of the mysterious. While masculine and feminine are represented within each of the Elements, the consensus is that yin is the feminine.

If your chart is more yang, then you are inherently a doer, bold in action and extroverted, free to express both your emotions and your ingenuity. You are likely assertive and move in the direction of an end result or goal. Considered more masculine, yang energy is faster moving and lighter than that of yin.

Think about a seed planted in the dirt. There it collects resources, minerals and water, in the darkness of yin energy. Then when the seed is ready, its roots develop and yang energy takes over, propelling the seed's sprout through the top layer of soil to grow up and out into the light.

I love this metaphor for the 5 Elements, because I feel it captures their depth and simplicity at the same time. Each Element is its own entity. We can discover new depths and layers to ourselves within a single Element, by looking at what it does, its purpose and its medicine. We can also flow between the Elements in this way, one to the next, acknowledging their relationship to one another.

The Greek model of elements (Air, Water, Earth, Fire) is more static; your astrology and natal chart lock you into one possibility (I'm a Gemini with a Scorpio rising and crazy amount of Air in my chart). The 5 Elements allow for more flow. You may be constitutionally a Water, but that doesn't mean you don't have a relationship to Wood or any other Element. You may cultivate or rely on an Element and its guidance at a particular moment in your life or for certain roles you have. In fact, an alternative translation for Elements in Chinese medicine is phases, which in some ways is more accurate, in that, like the seasons, one generates the next.

While it's true we contain all the Elements within us, we humans tend to get a little stuck. Due to life experiences and conditioning, we start to develop coping mechanisms early in life. We mirror our parents and peers to fit in, or perhaps do the exact opposite in a fit of self-definition.

What I've seen while doing this work is that our constitutional Element finds its dominance sometime in childhood, for a multitude of reasons.

1) Each Element is paired with particular organ systems and channels, so it's common for children born with congenital health issues to have their dominant Element be associated with the organ in

question. For example, children born with heart murmurs or other heart issues tend to have a predominant amount of Fire in their charts. Children with asthma, allergies, and immune issues associated with the lungs often have a lot of Metal in their charts.

2) Another way that dominant Elements can find their footing is through trauma, both physical and psychological. This is usually related to core requirements, which we will discuss in a little while. For the purposes of this discussion, it is enough to say that when certain needs aren't met physically, cognitively, emotionally, or spiritually, we will unconsciously seek ways to cope and fill these needs. Each Element seeks reconciliation differently. Therefore, depending on the trauma that occurred (and really nothing is too small here), the self will find comfort in some way, and through this process, may solidify a dominant Element.

3) Children mirror the adults in their life, either through like attracts like or opposites attract. Remember when you said you would never be like your mother. Well, it's likely you are either exactly like her or the complete opposite. It's very common for children to be spitting images of their parents or to seek to fill gaps within the family system to create better harmony and wholeness. We are adaptive beings; this is how we survive. It only makes sense that as children we seek a place within our family unit that provides us the best opportunity to thrive.

Before we go any further, it is important to highlight a unique aspect the 5 Elements, one that differentiates it from other personality assessments. In this system, there are always exceptions to the rule. Nothing is absolute. The 5 Elements aren't written in stone; they're phases, and they like to move around to find a better way to support us if they can.

So, let's discuss a few of the myriad ways that your dominant Element may shift and show up differently than what you're expecting.

Just like trauma, experiences inform your constitutional Element; they can also change it. If the coping mechanisms that you used in childhood no longer hold up to new challenges, then they will adapt. You may find yourself needing to fulfill other requirements to come back to center.

Life changes may also create a shift within you. In my acupuncture practice, I often see the charts of new mothers shift to show a greater predominance of Earth, as the Earth Element governs mothering and caretaking. It only makes sense that when babies are young and in constant need of their love and nourishment, their caretakers would cultivate more of this within themselves and feel Earth's pull. When their children begin to individuate, their chart may shift again to better address what they require at that time.

Another example that I've witnessed in my practice occurs when an individual gets incredibly ill and begins to contemplate their mortality. These individuals will often find their charts incorporating more Metal – as Metal initiates us to surrender all the things that don't matter. This in turn creates room to appreciate what's truly important. In the space of the Metal energy, we can realize with a renewed spirit what life is and, if given the chance, how we might choose to live it.

Essentially our Alchemy is reflective of what we value and experience in our lives at any given moment. As we grow and develop, some parts of our Alchemy solidify and stay with us, guiding and holding space for us to heal and relate to ourselves and the world. This relationship might be lifelong. Other parts of our Alchemy will change, like the seasons, as the Elements show up when we need them and then fall away when we don't.

Your Alchemy chart holds the keys to who you are and why you are the way you are. It can help you open up and express yourself – the real you – in new and exciting ways. It's possible that until now, you've been beating yourself up for your quirks or for not measuring up in a particular way. Enough of that.

You are perfect, just as you are.

Having this chart in front of me has helped me stop asking myself, "What's wrong with me?" Learning about my unique Alchemy has empowered me to take a stand for who I am. When I honor my Alchemy, I let it support me, my life, and what I desire. This has been replicated with my clients, which means it's possible for you too.

Your 5 Element Alchemy at a Glance

Looking at your individual Alchemy chart, I invite you to notice where your energy is and where it's not.

- Which Elements have the highest numbers? Identify your most dominant one.
- How many secondary Elements do you have? How great a separation is there between your dominant one and your secondaries?
- What Elements are most deficient?
- Are you more yin, with higher numbers in Earth, Metal and Water? Or are you more yang with higher numbers in Water, Wood and Fire?

As you traverse the next few chapters of this book, you will begin to understand the energetics of each Element and how you are pulled to work with them in your life.

A Few Notes Before We Move On

It's important to remember that we will be generalizing about the themes of each Element. These generalizations are useful because they help us understand these energies in their natural order and rhythm, and also how we may be working against them. Your dominant Element or Elements (depending on how close they are to each other) can be your superpower, but they also likely hold your greatest weaknesses, the places where you get most stuck.

I'm inviting you to use this information to realize how to strengthen and support your strengths and nurture your weaknesses from a place that respects your inherent wisdom and the essence of your soul. If you are new to the 5 Elements, my advice is to first acknowledge what your dominant Element is. Consider the ways it is functioning well, so you can foster more of that type of energy. How does it benefit you? Then look at where it's not working to its optimal potential.

Because the Elements exist in relationship with each other, we are not isolated from the ones that appear to have less influence on our self-expression and everyday actions and decisions. In fact, it's important to address how the other Elements impact us by either pulling us off center and away from trusting ourselves or by stagnating our growth and capacity for greater impact because they are under-utilized.

Use the writing prompts throughout this book to facilitate greater understanding of who you are through the lens of the 5 Elements and your Alchemy. They will reveal insights into how to live without apology and embrace the journey home to your soul to create a life fueled by love.

Chapter 2

The Earth Type

Peacekeeper – Caretaker – Mother

An Earth type is a natural nurturer. Caring for others – close friends, family, children – comes easily for them. They're a safe place to lay your head and take comfort. They also feel inclined to bring harmony to their environment and the people with whom they come in contact. I joke with my Earth clients that no one can take care of people the way an Earth can. They all giggle, but they know it's true. They just don't want others to feel bad, so they keep it under wraps. Earths like to have every detail under their thumb, not in a rigid and controlling sort of way but more so they can thoughtfully anticipate the needs of others and ensure that their guests and those around them want for nothing. They aspire to create a space where everyone can relax, put their feet up, leave their worries at the door, and feel at home. Meanwhile, the Earth type is busy running around, trying to figure out other ways they can make someone's day or experience more enjoyable.

An Earth type's gifts can be experienced in the details, ambience, sound, smell, and comfort they curate to ensure that each guest is made to feel welcome. As an Earth type, I have put thought into every detail of my acupuncture clinic. My intention is that – upon entering, before we've even started the treatment – each client feels as though they've arrived at an oasis where they can remove their armor and allow themselves to be supported. You know you're in the presence of an Earth when you're offered a drink, food, or a tissue, and asked a million and one times if you are okay. Earths take pleasure in being able to support others, and it's best to accept their support. This is just what they do. When an Earth is in balance, their support and compassion are unconditional. When they're not, they have a tendency to smother others by taking their caretaking to the extreme or becoming a martyr.

An Earth type has a special ability to meet everyone in the middle, supporting them where they're at. They don't impose their agenda on others or try to change them. Tenderly and compassionately, they accept you as you are in this moment – nothing more, nothing less. This quality speaks to their innate skill as a mediator. They often assume the role of the peacemaker or the glue that holds together a family, a group of friends, or even colleagues. They have a natural ability to find common ground. However, the ease with which they create harmony for others can easily lead to a tendency to people please, even when it's not in their best interest to do so. It can also lay the foundation for codependent relationships, where they avoid bringing attention to how others need to improve. Instead, they may just make other people's ruts more comfortable. When this has occurred, Earth types can struggle to break the ties that bind them to those they love. Witnessing another person struggle to actualize their own transformation when they know that they could help can make an Earth type feel as though they are withholding their love and affection. In fact, it's the complete opposite. Sometimes there is no greater gift – or sign of love and respect – than not to interfere.

Earth types will go to great lengths behind the scenes to bring to fruition everything from events to reconciliations between enemies. Again, the smallest details are thought out and executed to allow everyone present to relax and hopefully enjoy themselves. This positioning also makes Earth types great listeners and secret keepers. Because they are easy to confide in, put others at ease, and provide support, they are often who people approach to unburden their minds and feel better. They are also a safe choice. Because an Earth prides themselves on being the person that everyone turns to, they are a locked vault.

The only time this becomes problematic for an Earth is when they have been burdened with too many secrets – especially the worst type of secrets for an Earth, those that cause conflict or disharmony among a group or family. Desperate to keep their word to not share something – or to avoid burdening another by spilling the beans – Earths may find the secrets eating away at them. To help quell the disharmony they feel, an Earth will often use food, especially sweets or other numbing agents, to compensate. This is why self-care is such a valuable exercise for an Earth type. It allows them to reorient themselves back to their center and remember that they are just as important in their relationships as the people they care for.

Imbalances of the Earth Element

When the Earth Element is not in harmony, individuals will often experience issues with their digestive systems. This makes sense because the Earth Element governs the spleen and stomach channel in Chinese medicine. Common symptoms include abdominal distention, pain, inconsistent bowel movements lacking form, gas, belching, and changes in appetite. The Earth Element and its corresponding channels can also affect a woman's menstrual cycle and cause irregular periods and spotting.[5]

When an individual's inner Earth is overburdened, they may be consumed with overthinking and worrisome thoughts. These can cause them to struggle with making decisions, or to be unable to compartmentalize their thoughts, creating an overall feeling of being unclear and confused.[6]

Overthinking and Paralysis

Each Element type has a dominant emotion associated with their way of coping. An Earth type's emotional coping expression is pensiveness.

---

[5] Hick A., & Hicks J. (1999). *Healing your emotions.* Thorsons.

[6] Dechar, L. (2006). *Five spirits.* Lantern Books.

Because Earths spend so much energy anticipating what others need and making sure everything is okay, they can often get stuck in their heads, continuously ruminating over hundreds of scenarios that are mostly out of their control.

When they're up against unknown factors, they may fixate on worst-case scenarios, making mountains out of molehills and stirring up anxiety that causes them to lose sleep or experience full-blown panic attacks. Earth types can also become victims to analysis paralysis – unable to get their ideas or intentions past the initial thought process. This can leave them feeling like the King or Queen of Ideas without Action.

In either case, it's incredibly important for an Earth type to use tools, actions and supports to help them find focus. Once they are able to compartmentalize their thoughts, their mind has an easier time coming back to center and the present moment. To do this, they need to ground themselves and narrow their thoughts to truths within their control, while employing pragmatic and steady steps and actions that they can do right away. One strategy they can use to clear their head and take action in the direction of a harmonious and inspired life is to ask themselves: What is true for me right now, and what is one action I can do to improve my circumstances?

Caretaking in Right Relationship

Taking care of people is an Earth type's thing; they're good at it, and it comes easily to them. Outside of their family life, Earth types often choose professions where they can embody the same energetic, such as teachers, nurses, aides, and other caretaker roles. They don't usually choose roles or jobs where they would be front and center. They would much rather be behind the scenes orchestrating all of the details to ensure that everything comes together perfectly.

Earths take great pride in taking care of everyone; it fulfills a sense of purpose, and they love to witness others revel in their tender loving care and good intentions. However, if they get too wrapped up in satisfying everyone else, their cheerleading and caretaking roles can become detrimental to themselves. Abandoning their own evolution, ambitions and even self-care to assist others blossoming, they may find themselves sitting on the sidelines, watching life pass them by.

When this happens, it's easy for an Earth type's self-worth to become tied up with their ability to care for others. This can lead to a disharmonious relationship to caretaking that can result in an Earth smothering those they love. Their caretaking becomes about the Earth type wanting to feel useful and worthy, rather than what another person may want or need. This dynamic can also lead to an Earth type's kind heart and generosity being taken advantage of. If they are too good at their job and too invested in it, others may just assume that they will pitch in and take up the slack, without asking them if they want to help.

While it can be difficult to tease out whether a natural tendency and desire to support others is an impulse that has lost its integrity, most Earth types can benefit from considering how they can take care of their own needs while tending to everyone else's. I often encourage them to recognize how they would support and nurture someone they love and bestow that same kindness and care on themselves.

Saying NO as a Sentence

Most Earth types naturally overextend themselves to help others. Saying "yes" is as easy as breathing. Before the ask has even been completely articulated, they've enthusiastically agreed to it, even when they don't want to. An Earth type wants to make other people feel happy, and they like to be needed. Out of a sense of loyalty, a desire to be liked and appear agreeable, they will rise to meet others' requests.

For an Earth, saying "no" feels more uncomfortable than the alternative: feeling obligated or uninspired when they show up to help. The thoughts and feeling of disharmony that accompany letting someone down are unbearable to an Earth, so even when they manage to utter the word "no," they want to walk it back almost immediately. It doesn't matter if they've already said yes to way too many things and they're running themselves ragged. If everyone else is happy, they're happy, right?

Except of course there are occasions where an inability to say no is actually not helpful to themselves or others. For example, it can lead to codependent relationships where the Earth type thinks they are helping, but in fact, they are disempowering someone who is capable but hasn't yet had the opportunity to fulfill or reach their potential.

Often the only time an Earth type has uttered the word "no" is when they are so physically ill there is no way that they can manage. "No more!" they cry. But it shouldn't take such dire circumstances. In fact, I would argue that the ability to say no is key to an Earth type living their greatest life. "No" can be revolutionary. It may feel counterintuitive, but saying no is an equal if not greater way for Earth types to care for the people they love. While it may feel hard to say in the beginning, with practice, it gets much easier. Saying no is a boundary that enables an Earth type to put themselves first and actually check in and recognize where they want to spend their time, money and efforts. In time, they will be able to discern who and what is most important to them, how they wish to step in and help others, and where it's okay for them to hang back and prioritize themselves instead.

Great Expectations

Because an Earth is so exceptional at anticipating needs and providing support for others without them asking, it only makes sense that they would expect others to be thinking of them in the same ways. In other words, they tend to believe that those they love the most will reciprocate their care and meet their needs without them having to articulate those needs aloud. However, if they don't have other Earths within their immediate support system, this expectation often goes unmet. This can leave them feeling disappointed – or worse, trigger one of their greatest insecurities: the belief that no one cares about them.

Not wanting to inconvenience others, Earth types often struggle to articulate and express their own needs, even among the people they love the most. Because they believe that their needs don't matter as much as everyone else's, they can convince themselves that they don't have needs at all. Even when help or support is offered, they will push it away, taking the view that they are just being bothersome and should figure it out on their own.

Over time, this can result in a passive-aggressive martyr identity, and their bubbling resentment, if it's not acknowledged and reconciled, can boil over to an explosive rage. Feeling overburdened by their caretaking roles, they may complain, whine, and express their discontent while offering no solutions nor allowing anyone to assist them in changing the situation.

The antidote, of course, is for an Earth type to speak up and ask for what they need.

If they are not being supported in a way they prefer, rather than giving up or doing it all themselves, they need to take the time to teach those around them how they wish to be cared for and appreciated. This can have immeasurable benefits. Most importantly, it allows an Earth to feel truly nourished and supported, and this in turn will expand their own capacities to care for others.

Change Is Hard

Change in general can be hard for Earth types; they prefer to keep a routine, are most comfortable with what they know, and don't feel compelled to rock the boat – particularly if it will result in disharmony among their immediate circle of influence. This resistance to evolve past what's working in the moment has the potential to make them too stable, sluggish and even complacent in their everyday experiences.

Why break what's not broken? is an Earth's guiding philosophy. While this is a fair and pragmatic assertion, it can ingrain stagnancy and redundancy within behaviors and beliefs. As a result, Earths may meet different perspectives and opposing viewpoints that could spur growth with stubbornness, standoffish attitudes, and indecision.

If they are pushed too far or too quickly, Earths will easily shut down, put up a wall, and become apathetic. They are often immune to explanations for the purpose of an upheaval. Instead, they may make up excuses or dig in by finding ways to prove that the old way of doing things was better. This way they attempt to reinstitute order in their lives and return to their comfort zone. They may even choose to make cosmetic shifts to their environment. The purpose of these is to give an appearance of embracing change, to appease both their psyche and other people, while making no impactful adjustments. They are merely decorating their rut.

This is why Earth types often have to take a slower route to change. Using baby steps and repetition, they will get to the same place as others, however not with the same expediency. There is nothing wrong with slow and steady. By acknowledging their propensity to shy away from change and meeting this tendency with compassionate inquiry and a practical timeline, Earth types can make small but manageable shifts gracefully.

Searching for Home

For an Earth type, home has two equally important meanings. One is the embodied feeling of home they find within their own bodies. The other is a physical place where they seek refuge and create a life and family. Depending on life experiences, either can feel like a comfort or an elusive goal to seek.

Let's start by discussing the notion of the body as home. It is common for Earth types to fall in and out of right relationship with their bodies, always feeling never quite fully home there. They often have a sense of something missing, particularly at their center – triggering a weak or empty feeling at their belly or solar plexus. When this feeling occurs, they can struggle to trust their gut or stand up for themselves. They may feel uncertain and shaky about their intentions and decisions, and begin to question their beliefs and opinions. Earth types often become chameleons or shapeshifters to appease others and create harmony. This leaves them vulnerable to taking on others' definitions of who they are or what they want, further perpetuating the inability to feel at home with and within themselves.

Earth types are also very sensitive and particular about their physical spaces. They seek a home base where they can settle, become grounded, and grow roots for themselves and the people they love. The energetics and feng shui of a room can have an incredible impact on how an Earth type feels about a space and themselves. To increase their sense of being centered and grounded, it can be healing for an Earth type to go through the process of making a house a home and integrating their loving energy into a physical space.

Earths, however, can sometimes misinterpret this longing for home – believing that the perfect place, decor, location, etc., is going to fix what they feel is lacking in them, rather than cultivating a sense of center within themselves first. This will lead them to a constant state of upheaval – moving multiple times, always traveling and living out of their suitcase, unable to settle anywhere long enough to put down roots and create a life that embodies their truest essence. When circumstances aren't favorable to establish a home physically or as an embodied felt sense, Earths can benefit from connecting to the earth itself, through gardening and caretaking the planet. This can provide an invitation to nurture and broaden the definition of what home can mean. After all, the earth is our ultimate home, always nourishing and supporting us to grow and thrive.

Keeping Promises to Everyone, Including Themselves

Earth types are incredibly hard working, dependable and loyal. It brings them much joy to put their head down and lend a helping hand where they are needed. They subscribe to the motto that there is no "I" in team and will do everything they can to create a harmonious work environment for everyone involved. They will cheerlead team members when they need it and support anyone who is struggling.

Where an Earth type themselves is likely to get stuck is when they are confronted by the bigger picture. Too much information can leave them feeling overwhelmed and unsure as to how best to move forward. This can cause them to get stuck in their heads, ruminating about all the work and tasks that need to occur, without ever taking action. This in turn creates a belief within that they lack follow-through.

In moments such as these, it's important for Earths to clear distractions, such as clutter and commitments that aren't obligatory, and start with small steady steps that help them organize their thoughts and actions. As they complete each task, they will establish confidence in themselves, garnering momentum to keep going. This is especially helpful when an Earth type would be the main beneficiary of the outcome. It's their own passion and heart's desire they're pursuing.

Earth types may find it helpful to schedule times in their calendar to devote to their work unencumbered by other responsibilities, i.e. work, kids, spouse, etc. This alleviates any unnecessary guilt they have about putting themselves first. Scheduling time to listen to one's heart and work toward dreams and goals need be no different or harder than scheduling a dentist appointment. It is a necessary component of self-care. Doing this often will lift an Earth up and create a ripple effect of outcomes that extend beyond their initial intention, allowing others to thrive and rise alongside them.

Healing Tools for Your Inner Earth

Self-care: You can't give to others what you don't give to yourself. It is essential that you make time to take care of yourself. Rest, take a bath, walk in nature, spend a few moments journaling when the house is quiet – mother your own ideas and desires as you would mother those of others.

Connect with Your Element: An Earth's constitution holds a profound affinity to the earth that must be nurtured for an Earth type to feel secure. Putting one's feet or hands in the dirt, tending to a garden, and stargazing are all ways to connect to the earth's potent energy and experience incredible healing.

Earth Meditation: Standing on the earth with your bare feet apart, your legs slightly bent, allow the earth energies to enter your body through your feet. The extra connection to the earth gained from this simple stance can be healing and supportive, enabling you to feel more secure, balanced and centered inside.

Learn the Word NO: Use it as a sentence.[7] You don't need to even provide an explanation. Notice how hard it is for you to let the word hang out there. And then do it again! Challenge yourself to say five no's before one yes. This will help you to discern what you really want to say yes to and free you up to actually do it, rather than filling your time with activities and actions you've agreed to out of a sense of obligation.

Yawn: There are many explanations for the possible causes and reasons for yawning. What I have experienced and noticed is that yawning helps to ground and open up the mind for new thought. Try it. Start the action of yawning and notice the sensations as the yawn travels up into the brain and then back down the body. Relax into the clarity that it provides and the centeredness it creates within your body.

---

[7] Dechar, L. (2006). *Five spirits.* Lantern Books.

Innate Strengths of an Earth Type[8]

- Mother energy embodied
- Experiences ease in supporting and caretaking others
- Selfless and compassionate; easily puts others before themselves
- An ability to make a house a home
- Enjoys preparing and working with food
- Feels a deep connection to the earth
- Loyal and dependable

Opportunities for Growth for an Earth Type

- Excessively helpful and over-nourishing; smothering others when they don't need or want to be cared for
- Establishing boundaries
- Taking responsibility for their own needs; being willing to accept or ask for help
- Walking a fine line between supporting others and succumbing to the martyr complex
- Complacent; unwilling to make changes or move beyond what is comfortable
- Obsessive worrying and overthinking[9]

---

[8] The "innate strengths" and "opportunities for growth" that conclude each Element type chapter have been drawn from *Healing Your Emotions* by Hicks and Hicks (1999), as well as observations made in my professional practice.

[9] Hicks, A., & Hicks, J. (1999). *Healing your emotions.* Thorsons.

Chapter 3

The Metal Type

Artist — Architect — Alchemist

Of all the Element types, I believe that Metals are the most misunderstood. Even when someone identifies themselves as a Metal in a group, they tend to do so in a slightly begrudging, self-deprecating way. Apologizing for not being as fun as the Fires or as friendly as the Earths. Sometimes they are just outright miscast as a Wood type (though it's my opinion that Metals tend to be quieter and shyer). If you have Metal as your dominant Element or even your secondary, I want to start by telling you that you can stop apologizing for what you aren't. The Metal Element is beautiful in its own right, necessary even. The world needs Metals, and I'm hoping that after reading this chapter dedicated to you, you will see yourself as I do.

A large part of why Metals tend to apologize for not being someone else is because they are motivated to be recognized and feel adequate. They don't usually find accolades and recognition in rooms full of other people because they tend to shy away from the spotlight. But all human beings want to be liked and included. Even though they may appear distant from the outside, Metals do too. And if they tend to have difficulty expressing their emotions, it doesn't mean that those emotions aren't there.

Often reserved, quiet and a bit standoffish to strangers, Metal types can be difficult to get to know. They don't offer much in the form of small talk. They are protective of themselves and what they say, because behind that more rigid, conservative exterior is actually a very sensitive and vulnerable personality. Criticism can feel really harsh for a Metal. They choose their words and actions carefully and purposefully, and because of that, they take the words and actions of others the same way.

Some people wouldn't give a second thought to a joke or an off-the-cuff comment made about them. A Metal type may take it as a direct reflection of who they are, analyzing and dissecting it to the nth degree, so that they can reconcile how it was meant. If they decide improvements to themselves can be made, they will make the necessary corrections. Metals often feel that it's best to say little, as to not open themselves up to possible criticism or ongoing discussion, especially when a smile and handshake will suffice.

Now if you're lucky enough to be included within a Metal's inner circle, then it's a totally different story. Metal types remove their armor and relax in the presence of people they feel supported by or close to. They can melt and transform before your eyes. Metals do appreciate conversation, particularly if it's centered around something they care deeply about or have opinions on. Blessed with a way with words, most Metals that I have come to know have a witty, somewhat dry sense of humor, with a flair for sarcasm.

A Metal's actions aren't grandiose, and they have absolutely no bandwidth for drama. Instead, they convey their affection and intention in more subtle ways that nevertheless often result in the most profound impacts. This is due to the overarching governance of the Metal Element, which connects us to the present moment and reveals its preciousness and significance. Making the ordinary extraordinary is one of the Metal type's talents. They accomplish this through a strong sense of presence and reverence.

Not overly impulsive or spontaneous, Metals aren't known for throwing elaborate surprise parties for loved ones. They prefer to plan and have control over their environment whenever possible. Knowing what's coming helps Metals secure their autonomy, make choices and anticipate their actions. Always wanting to put their best foot forward, Metals can find themselves riddled with anxiety when faced with the potential chaos of a surprise. While other types may feel constrained by structures and procedure, Metals feel the complete opposite. Structure provides the container within which they can surrender, be vulnerable, and allow their creativity to thrive.

Imbalances of the Metal Element

When the Metal Element is not in harmony, the first physical symptoms are likely to be related to the immune system. Metal governs the lungs and large intestine in Chinese medicine, so it's common to see disharmony manifest as a propensity to catch colds and flus, experiencing allergic reactions in response to environmental factors, or being susceptible to asthma, bowel disturbances, and skin sensitivities. Individuals experiencing disharmony of the Metal Element may also experience stress-related tension and an overall restlessness, clouded mind, and impairment to their balance, movement, and coordination.

When the mental and emotional capacities of the Metal Element are unsupported, obsessions, depression, anxiety, and eating disorders may result, due to the rigidity and structure that a Metal type may employ to protect themselves.[10]

It's All in the Details

Metal types find significance in and pay attention to small details. They like everything to have its place and be where it is meant to be. They double- and triple-check their work to ensure there are no errors. This precision is woven into most of a Metal type's life – from their wardrobe, to how they choose to furnish their home, to the ways they present themselves and their work to others.

Clean lines and simplicity are how Metal types prefer to approach all tasks. Why clutter up something's inherent beauty with a bunch of stuff that doesn't need to be there? They're constantly refining themselves and their environment to seek greater efficiency and the ultimate

---

[10] Dechar, L. (2006). *Five spirits.* Lantern Books.

utilization of resources to create the most impact. Absolute perfection is the goal whenever possible.

While others may tire of the tediousness that some high-detail work requires, a Metal type's patience and innate drive to completion are foundational to their success. They take the philosophy that the more intimate you can become with the details, the greater the potential for feeling fulfilled and being recognized for your efforts.

This philosophy can, however, work against them at times. They may find themselves getting too caught up with the task at hand, looking for details and implementing unnecessary procedures and extra steps. This can inhibit their ability to progress and see a task through to completion.

It's Okay to Color Outside the Lines

Metals types prefer order and control in their lives whenever possible. Rules bring them a sense of comfort, allowing them to relax, because it is clear what the expectations are for themselves and others. Rules also serve as a form of protection against unforeseen chaos or drama. There is nothing inherently wrong with this affinity; however, rules and a desire for control can close in on Metal types and insulate them against others and the world. Trapped in a very small bubble, they can struggle to take in new information, people, or experiences that may provide insight or opportunities to evolve past what they already know.

When combined with a Metal's tendency to become overly rigid and righteous when stressed, their adherence to rules they create or adopt can make them a prisoner in a jail of their own making. Believing that they have found the right and pure way to live, work, and love, they may weave their beliefs into all aspects of their life, including routine, food, work, environment, movement, and prayer. This lens will inform everything – from how small tasks should be executed to the right way to live one's life. When Metals fail to live up to the often very strict confines and expectations they've set – falling off the righteous path – they will chastise themselves. They may also impose these rules on others and chastise them when they too falter.

To assist a Metal in navigating their tendencies toward rigidity, it's important to remember that even though metals may appear hard, solid and structured, they can all be transformed. Metal can be melted down, rock can be chiseled, clay can be molded. Just because what appears before you is in one form doesn't mean that there isn't even greater beauty waiting to be uncovered. A container and rules that worked for a Metal type in the past may not support them in the future. While the initial desire to enact some control was to protect and perhaps heal a part of themselves, a Metal who doesn't allow for organic shifts in their life and identity, and in others, may only further exacerbate the deficiencies and fragility that were there to begin with.

Nothing Short of Perfection

We've already touched on a Metal type's drive for perfection, but it's important that we delve into where this drive comes from. Perfection – or at least the perception that it exists – allows a Metal type to feel protected; it shields them like armor. It also creates an illusion that they can insulate their ego from criticism. If they can just say and do the perfect thing, then how could anyone criticize them? In this way, they attempt to avoid being hurt.

At times, Metals may find themselves motivated to do their best and position themselves above others as compensation or a trade-off for the instances when they feel they lack personality or an ability to show warmth and camaraderie among groups and in their relationships. While others may interpret this as pretentious or snobby, it's actually a learned behavior to mask deeper insecurities.

Perfection, however, can wreak havoc with a Metal's life, in part because perfection is often impossible. Having incredibly high standards and expecting nothing less than 100 percent from themselves and everyone around them can create animosity and friction within their relationships. This may result in alienating themselves from those they love because of an impression that others are not measuring up or meeting their impeccably high standards.

The quest for perfection can be a slippery slope to feeling resignation or cynicism toward all things. When you expect perfection but rarely achieve it, it can eventually wear down your self-esteem. Metals may find themselves believing that they will never be good enough or worthy of their desires. This negative outlook may push them to shut down in an attempt to distance themselves from their own disappointment.

But it's not all doom and gloom. A Metal's pursuit of perfection can be admirable. After all, pushing oneself to do and be better is the premise of self-improvement and how one masters a skill. This natural tendency serves them well in many areas of their life. They may not find perfection, but they often achieve excellence. When I help my Metal-type clients navigate their desire for perfection, I often ask them: Is wanting perfection in a particular area of life helpful? Or is it inhibiting their progress? By applying this question to an individual task or objective, they can start to let some things go, thereby creating room to engage their attention and discipline with a pursuit that is more worthwhile.

Breathe It In

As a natural result of their hard work and perseverance, Metal types are often extremely accomplished, at the top of their class and field. It's no surprise that with such prestige comes massive accolades, hardware, and recognition for their efforts.

Being recognized in this way is a core requirement of the Metal type, and one of the reasons they push themselves so hard to succeed. However, even though they aspire for acknowledgment – and many other Element types would be celebrating and basking in the spotlight – Metals tend to struggle with taking in positive affirmations and rewards.

Metals are usually quite introverted and shy, which is why they may feel a bit awkward or uncomfortable being center stage. When an appearance is required, they tend to come across as humble and reserved.

As a result of their perfectionist tendencies, they can also be dismissive of their talents and the awards they receive. If they believe that they could have done more or achieved a higher level of excellence, they may struggle to wholeheartedly accept the accolades they have been given. Which is why it is helpful for Metal types to stop and take a moment to breathe it all in. Even if they perceive an accomplishment as a stepping stone to greater heights and mastery, by acknowledging their efforts, they can achieve closure so that new inspiration can fully integrate itself on the next step of their journey.

Seeking Meaning

Despite looking put together and appearing to have the answers, Metal types are inherently seekers. They have big questions they want to understand, which often brings them to seek a connection with their divinity. Finding meaning is another core requirement for the Metal Element. When their world doesn't make sense, they find comfort in the concepts of spirit, a guiding universal energy, or a God of their own understanding.

Surrendering to something bigger than themselves – that they can't necessarily control – gives a Metal type permission to be vulnerable. And channeling their energies toward being a steward of a grander plan can instill a sense of purpose. This can propel them to become students exploring the vastness of knowledge in the hopes of discovering the truth. By which I mean the truth of the universe – the underlying meaning to why we are all here – and the truth of themselves as an individual – their particular purpose and role in the design.

On their quest to know, they may have opportunities to join organizations they feel align with their intentions, be led to teachers they aspire to follow, and be introduced to beliefs, practices, and rituals to accentuate their connection to the Divine and their own knowing. Depending on the circumstances that have caused them to seek (particularly, in times of great stress and emotional crisis), they may find it easy to suspend critical thinking and dismiss internal cues that they are being led astray. When you want an answer or direction so badly, to stop hurting, it is easy to grasp at what's available, even if it's not in your best interest.

If the path to righteousness causes a Metal to cut away or let go of parts of their life that contradict a set of teachings or belief system, it is best to take inventory and ask why. Is letting go of relationships, jobs, practices, or possessions bringing them closer to their humanity and soul's expression? Or are they idolizing a false prophet and thus preventing their soul's unique expression?

Optimizing Productivity and Purpose

Structure, definition, discipline, pragmatism, purpose – these are qualities and values many Metal types subscribe to. They tend to prefer when the pieces fit together and make sense. To optimize productivity and stability, Metals turn to lists, sequential steps and clear objectives – strategies that help bring about completion and success.

Objectivity and an ability to keep their emotions out of the decision-making process enable them to assess all working parts of a project or task, so they can implement a strategy to bring it all together in the most efficient manner, while ensuring that high-quality workmanship remains a priority. Batching and chunking techniques are examples of helpful tools a Metal will use to assist them in accomplishing their tasks and not getting overwhelmed by the mountain of work they may have. With each completed task, they build the foundation to continue toward their intended goal.

Connecting to the purpose of a task or job is incredibly helpful for a Metal. Without this connection, they will tend to feel lost and complacent, unsure of how they can effectively do a good job when it's unclear why they are doing it and how their efforts will contribute to an outcome. Driven by their core requirement of needing to feel adequate, they can flounder without clear direction. This can culminate in feeling unworthy and that they are not a valuable asset.

Metal types do well in most roles within an organization. They work well both individually and in groups. On their own, they are self-directed and disciplined. They keep their focus, remain on task, and complete their work as expected. If they're required to learn a new skill, they will set a course to figure it out to the point where they feel competent and can execute it with ease.

They can confidently lead when they feel they have the expertise and credentials needed. As a result of their pursuit of higher learning and expertise, they often find themselves in managerial or executive roles. They're also happy to be on a team, provided they feel that the leader is competent, effective, and worthy of their respect and that everyone else on the team is pulling their weight; otherwise, they would rather just do it all themselves.

Healing Tools for Your Inner Metal

Breathe: Developing a meditation or conscious breath practice helps to bring you back to the present moment. Quieting the noise both externally (from others) and internally (your own inner dialogue) will assist you in coming back to what's most important.

Gratitude Practice: At the end of the day, identify at least three things that you're thankful for and write them down. This exercise is designed to develop your capacity to take in good feelings, compliments, and respect in such a way that they nourish you and your core requirements. Daily appreciation of the positive will help you sharpen your awareness of other positive occurrences and cancel out any negativity. Over time this process will help to break down some of the self-criticism and cynicism that may be preventing you from finding the internal satisfaction you're seeking.

Performing Rituals: Rituals serve many purposes to support your inner Metal. They provide a structure to engage your spirit and an alchemical space to spur creativity and turn lead into gold. By allowing sacredness to occur in your daily devotions, such as journaling, meditation, prayer, pulling oracle cards, or movement, you have an opportunity to become present to the preciousness of each moment, while also connecting to the higher spirits or God of your own understanding. You may want to choose practices centered around letting go and surrendering control.

Practicing Imperfection: Unlearning perfection takes time; it is woven through so many aspects of life. So it's important to be gentle with yourself as you acknowledge how you are using perfection as a form of protection. Take the time to understand why your belief in perfection exists, before trying to remove it or disparage yourself for it. It can be helpful to take small steps in disabling patterns or beliefs. Allow yourself to be less curated – less perfect – in person, on social media, and in other areas where you show up. Choose activities that grant you permission to be a beginner or make mistakes. These may help uncover and heal deeper emotions that may be seeking reconciliation through aspiring for perfection.

Grieve: Spend some time connecting to loss; allow yourself to cry, weep and sob. Make this a daily practice to help you move through any rigidities and beliefs that are constraining you. When we honor loss (even if it's just hypothetical), we can connect to the purpose behind our patterns and reaffirm our autonomy, so that we can create new beliefs and practices out of the old.

Innate Strengths of a Metal Type

- Hard-working and tenacious
- Appreciates competence, skill, and expertise
- Motivated by achieving personal excellence
- Can be objective and impartial
- A seeker of meaning and connection to the preciousness of life
- An affinity for words

Opportunities for Growth for a Metal Type

- Tend to be cold and withholding to the point of self-isolation when feeling the need to self-protect
- Highly critical with perfectionist tendencies
- Addicted to struggle; always moving the target of what is worthy
- Propensity for pessimism and cynicism
- Difficulty letting go of control
- A capacity for righteousness that inhibits experiencing ordinary life[11]

---

[11] Hicks, A., & Hicks, J. (1999). *Healing your emotions.* Thorsons.

Chapter 4

The Water Type

Philosopher — Dreamer — Mystic

Water types are philosophers, thinkers and observers. Much like the expanse of an ocean, water types are drawn to the depths of everything that they do. They don't care for anything superficial. They value intelligence, wisdom and insight, and when interacting with others, they long to do so in an honest, soulful and authentic way. To be as they are, raw and imperfect, is preferable to playing pretend and dancing around what really matters.

Usually quiet in group settings (if they actually show up for them), they prefer to be on the outskirts observing, rather than the center of attention. If they manage to find someone they can REALLY talk to, you will find them hidden away in a quiet corner the whole night, deep in conversation. Similar to Metal types, Waters can be a little difficult to get to know, as they are somewhat hard to pin down. This is in part because they naturally question others' motivations for wanting to get to know them. They wish to figure out if the other person is being authentic and what they expect from them. Waters don't usually fall into the trap of needing to people please. If they are unable to get a good read on someone, then they have no qualms about keeping them at arm's length. However, if they assess an individual's intentions as pure, they will easily bring them into their inner circle.

Waters often carry an aura of reverence and wisdom; others look to them for insight and answers. Usually well studied, and connected to their divinity through practices that support their beliefs, they give really good advice. They are always asking thought-provoking questions to get at the essence of what someone is seeking, so they can respond with profound depth, often creating great impact in the advice-seeker's life.

They require generous moments of silence and stillness in their everyday lives. This helps them to quell agitation in their nervous system so that they may come back to their natural rhythm of trusting in themselves and the divine order. Cultivating practices of meditation and stillness restores their ability to listen to their intuition and reflect on their current circumstances, unencumbered by others' expectations, to gain perspective on what is aligned with their soul. This helps them tap into bigger-picture and source energy to strengthen their resolve to move forward with their plans with faith and courage, while mediating any necessary risks.

When out of harmony with their Element, a Water type will become fearful, withdrawing and walling themselves off from others to self-protect. They are naturally already introverted and aloof. They like to be by themselves, and so it can be easy for others to misjudge when they've gone off grid in search of solitude and when they require support and someone should follow up or go after them. This is why it's so important for Waters to seek supportive relationships that keep them connected to the happenings of the wider world.

Water types shine in a crisis. Their capacity to overcome adversity and difficulty is truly astonishing. Blessed with courage and coolheadedness, in the midst of chaos, they often take on the role of reassuring others, and offer steady and stable direction to help guide themselves and everyone else to calmer waters.

Imbalances of the Water Element

In Chinese medicine, the Water Element governs kidneys, bladder, bones, reproduction, and the aging phases of life. Imbalances to this Element manifest in the body as a sore back, issues with the spine, difficulties with urination, swollen legs, poor energy or lethargy, adrenal fatigue, night sweats, extreme thirst, lack of libido, infertility, and premature aging.[12]

The mental emotional capacities that are affected when the Water Element is unsupported include general forgetfulness, lack of motivation or initiative, an inability to stay the course when faced with difficulty, addictive patterns, depression, fear, sleep disturbances, and an inability to cope with change, leading to a nervous breakdown.[13]

Fear/Fearlessness Is Their Middle Name

A Water type's expression largely hinges on their perception of safety. How safety is defined and what it means varies based on the individual. Regardless, Water types are always eager to assess the risks before deciding whether to leap or remain where they are.

When they feel safe, Waters are pretty much up for anything, as long as it's within the parameters they have set for themselves. This means that Water types at the riskier end of the spectrum can be complete daredevils, risking life and limb to jump out of a plane or swim in a cage with sharks. These Waters are always pushing the envelope in search of the next thrill. They live for the pumping of adrenaline through their bodies.

Water types can also be the most timid and scared people in the room. Fear is the governing emotion of the Water Element. If a Water type lacks the ability to assess the risks or isn't able to trust themselves, they can become paralyzed. As next steps arise, they are unable to take them. Instead of leaping at opportunities, they turn away from them.

While most Waters will find themselves somewhere in the middle of these extremes, their life experiences will inform or dictate how they navigate circumstances as they arise. Their past relationships to fear, risk, and (un)certainty will govern their decisions on how best to circumvent or overcome obstacles and move toward their authentic expression in each moment.

---

[12] Hicks, A., & Hicks, J. (1999). *Healing your emotions.* Thorsons.

[13] Dechar, L. (2006). *Five spirits.* Lantern Books.

Knower of All Things

A Water type is a knower of things. They relax by reading and learning, experiencing great joy when diving deep and discovering the meaning beneath the meaning. Curious and always asking questions, they are seekers of truth and yearn to uncover the mysteries of the universe.

Due to the vastness of knowledge that they collect, Water types are often seen as wisdom keepers. Others may look to Waters when they need advice or direction. They are able to offer reassurance and guidance without being attached to what someone decides to do with that information. However, because they are so well informed, Waters' sage advice is often trusted and taken.

Because of this ability to influence, it is wise for Waters to remember to stay grounded and authentic in how they choose to share their advice. Others may put them on a pedestal or worship them as a guru. However, Waters who abdicate their own internal inquiry and self-discovery will be separated from their humanity, setting them up for a fall, either due to their own egotism or another's transference.

Another pitfall Waters may encounter is overvaluing knowing over doing. Waters may come to believe that researching and just knowing how to do something are enough. They don't feel a need to go out and prove that they can actually do it. This can perpetuate a pattern where they never choose to take the information they've acquired and turn it into action. As a result, they may have a false sense of bravado or ego about their capabilities with no true evidence for them. To progress, evolve, and grow, Waters who find themselves in this situation need to engage in self-inquiry to determine what they intend to do with the information they have learned.

Let It Be Easy

Waters tend to go with the flow and seek ease, believing that more often than not the path of least resistance is best. With their capacity to remain slightly detached from outcomes, Waters are often serendipitously in the right place at the right time, the best options becoming available to them as if by magic.

When they are listening to their intuition and trusting the next steps as they appear, Waters are able to follow the invocations of their soul to make decisions that are true to them, which usually, ultimately, leads to good outcomes. If they cut themselves off from their inner wisdom or attempt to force something that isn't aligned with their values, resistance and hardship will follow.

That doesn't mean that Waters don't have to work and take initiative to reach their goals. Waters need to keep an open mind when faced with resistance. They are inclined, when unable to cope or figure out how to overcome a challenge, to convince themselves that it's an alignment issue. This gives them permission to give up or excise the difficulty, so they can continue to ride the wave of good vibes and only engage with the areas of their lives that have come together with little to no effort. But just because something is hard doesn't mean it's the wrong thing to do.

Used to experiencing ease and flow most of the time, Waters can be lured into complacency and a lack of ambition, unwilling to put in the slightest effort the moment it gets a little bit challenging. This can cause them to abandon their endeavors in pursuit of areas where they just seem to fall into success.

To shift this dynamic, Waters may find it helpful to take a step back and look at their circumstances holistically. What old stories come up when they are faced with an obstacle? What's triggering their resistance to resistance? What's keeping them from really trying at something new? Perhaps it is time to surrender some of these old ideas and start healing. Being curious and taking self-inventory, as well as noticing how trouble in a particular area may fit into larger patterns in their life, may help Waters both recognize and interrogate their tendencies toward complacency. They may also want to take a breather or a short time away from the problem. This will allow them to come back to it with fresh eyes and usually find a solution that helps them rediscover flow in the direction of their goal.

Leaping into Uncertainty

Waters have an uncanny ability to assess risk and take a leap of faith toward their destiny, even when it's uncertain how all the pieces will come together. Regardless of how big the leap is (or whether it could more accurately be described as a small, steady step), they exhibit courage and unwavering faith that there will be a net to catch them on the other side. No matter what happens, they fully believe they will be okay.

To an outsider, some of their decisions and actions can seem completely reckless. What they don't know is that the Water type has already anticipated all of the foreseeable obstacles they might encounter and has planned out how they will behave or respond if they occur. Naturally, they could still be surprised by something that hadn't entered their realm of possibility. However, if they have marshaled their resources and developed the mindset necessary to stand on the edge and get ready to leap, they are supported by a deeper knowing, like an invisible bridge, that will deliver them safely to the other side, triumphant.

It's an entirely different situation when fear is plaguing their consciousness and clouding their ability to see clearly. If this occurs, the only outcomes they may be able to consider are ones where they meet disaster of epic proportions. Fraught with imagining failure and worst-case scenarios, a Water will become paralyzed and unable to move forward into the unknown, instead choosing to remain where they are.

If fear is interfering with their ability to know what comes next for them, Water types should do what they do best: ask more questions, seek support of a mentor or coach to help guide them around their blocks, and understand why the fear persists. Once they've reconciled their fears and brought them back down to a manageable level, they will feel safe to trust themselves and be able to put their energy behind their next steady step and take inspired action.

Freedom to Be

Being contractually obligated beyond what feels authentic will have a Water type looking for the exit. The need to feel free is one of the core requirements of the Water Element, and a constant area of negotiation in their lives. After all, freedom can be difficult to attain. Waters never want to be pigeonholed into a position, commitment, or role that leaves no room for growth or an opportunity to reassess if their values or attitudes have shifted. Wary of unwanted attachment, they will avoid making commitments if they don't know if they can keep them.

Waters also like to make space for opportunities to take off and experience freedom and solitude whenever their soul requires it. The idea of a silent retreat, or a trip to the middle of nowhere to be by themselves, is dreamy. Time away spent wandering and in deep reflection helps recharge their batteries, so that when they come back, they have new perspective, and are refreshed, present, and engaged with the tasks at hand.

This is why most Waters I know tend to prefer to keep plans and calendars open, with lots of space to honor their own needs and to follow their flow. Having everything scheduled to the nth degree and knowing where they will be a year from now would be enough to overwhelm most Waters and make them want to check out completely. Even when it's likely they will be doing the same activity on a given day that they might have planned and scheduled months in advance, they prefer to just take it as it comes – one day at a time. This way, they can be open to information and events that haven't yet entered their consciousness to manifest in their own divine timing.

Workflow and Alignment

When it comes to work and projects, it should come as no surprise that a Water type prefers, whenever possible, to work by themselves. That way they can trust their own workflow and allow adequate time to reflect and think through all the different ways they can accomplish their task before settling on the best one. They can then pace themselves properly to meet expectations.

Waters prefer timelines that provide flexibility and freedom, over those with fast and hard deadlines that may require them to burn the candle at both ends or, worse, put out work that doesn't reflect their knowledge or expertise. However, a Water type can fall prey to procrastinating and underestimating the amount of work required to complete a project. As a result, they may have to call on their inner adrenaline junkie to pull everything together at the last minute. If they rely on this part of themselves too often, it can be a nasty habit to break and may take some effort to reign it in.

Water types can also work alongside others. Just because it's not necessarily their preference doesn't mean it's not possible. Given their carefree, easygoing nature, they easily fit into a group setting. As a result of their inherent curiosity, they are generally highly skilled and multifaceted, making it easy for them to jump in and lend a hand where they are needed.

When it comes to careers, work, and projects, it is important that a Water believes in what they are supposedly working toward. Materialism and prestige aren't usually enough of an incentive for them to press ahead. If a company or brand is looking for a "yes man" who will fall in line and do what they're told, a Water type isn't going to maintain their position for very long. They want to do real work that makes a difference and aligns with their soul. Wealth and some aspects of materialism often fall into place to support their life as they follow what they feel is true, but these aren't the end goals, or reasons, to put their best foot forward.

Healing Tools for Your Inner Water

Spend Time with Water: Allow water to be your teacher[14]; notice how it ebbs and flows in the oceans, rivers, ponds, and streams of your local community. Witness how your body responds to listening to its sounds and seeing light reflecting off its surface. Allow yourself to journal any reflections or questions that arise as you take it all in.

Make Friends with Your Fear: What we resist persists. It's important to acknowledge your fears rather than trying to ignore them. Get familiar

---

[14] Dechar, L. (2006). *Five spirits.* Lantern Books.

with them; sit with them in meditation. Choose small practices or activities that allow you to develop trust around the people or situations that you find fearful.[15]

Shake: When a person experiences extreme shock or fear, they will often begin to shake. This is the body's instinctual way of dispelling the situation or experience to protect organs such as the adrenals and kidneys. By practicing shaking, you can access the fear you have internalized over your lifetime and ultimately release your attachment to it, both mentally and physically.

Foot Massage: The kidney channel is governed by the Water Element. Massaging the acupressure point Kidney 1, located at the bottom of the foot, will help relax the body by calming the spirit and replenishing its vitality.

Meditation and Stillness: It's important to devote time to sit in stillness every day. Quieting your mind will allow deep inner knowing to arise, which can help guide you toward your most authentic expression and the answers you seek. Choose to commit to just five minutes every day; you can stay longer when it feels good to do so. With time and practice, you will likely find that sitting in stillness becomes a non-negotiable component of your self-care.

---

[15] Dechar, L. (2006). *Five spirits.* Lantern Books.

Innate Strengths of a Water Type

- A capacity to evaluate safety and security
- Faces difficulties with determination and confidence
- Courageous in crisis situations
- Mediates risks and chooses the best path
- A capacity to see the big picture
- An affinity for seeking understanding of the deeper truths and mysteries of the universe
- Wisdom (others seek out their opinion and advice)

Opportunities for Growth for a Water Type

- Extremely fearful (concerned about all the possible ways something can go wrong)
- Faking bravado and confidence in precarious or dangerous situations
- Can underestimate or downplay apparent danger
- Tends to abandon projects and practice, in pursuit of new curiosities
- Can become ambition-less and apathetic[16]

---

[16] Hicks, A., & Hicks, J. (1999). *Healing your emotions.* Thorsons.

Chapter 5

The Wood Type

Leader — Warrior — Visionary

The Wood Element governs the spring season. This bustling yang energetic allows the emergence of the unseen as it bursts through the soil upwards toward the light. However you encounter the Wood Element – whether you identify as a Wood type or not – you will notice that its vibration is far different than the Elements we've previously covered. While those were more yin, this Element is all yang. The yang energetic is more assertive, a little bit in your face at times, partly because those with more yang in their Alchemy tend to want to be acknowledged and seen for who they are and what they do. While the more yin Elements – Earth, Metal and Water – are comfortable at the perimeter, waiting for the invitation to speak up and share, the yang Elements – Wood and Fire – take center stage. This is why you may find it easier to detect the Wood Elements in your life (the same is true of Fire types, which we discuss in the next chapter).

A Wood type has no time for waiting in the wings; they've got things to do. If there's an opportunity available to share who they are and what they're all about, they'll take it. If the opportunity doesn't present itself, a Wood type will happily create a platform, stage, or moment so they can share. The Wood type is a doer, a mover and a shaker. They don't get caught up in overthinking how something should be done; they just start doing it. Because they're a genuine self-starter, they are confident that they can figure it out as they go. If a problem arises, they fully believe a solution must be around the corner.

Their confidence is infectious and admirable, which allows a Wood type to easily find themselves in leadership roles, taking charge, delegating, and setting the pace with their can-do attitude. A Wood type is usually upbeat and positive, which works in their favor when they're leading the charge. This is why some of your favorite motivational speakers are Wood types. Need a pep talk? Look no further than the Wood type in your life. However, when their easy access to power gets the best of their ego, Wood types can be quite harsh and intolerant, even becoming irate if others don't meet their expectations or follow through with their plan. It's important for a Wood type to have people and practices in their life that remind them of their humility and innate benevolence.

A Wood type is unapologetic about who they are. Because of this, they may come across as blunt and a bit garish. People who don't know them may misunderstand them or perceive them as arrogant. However, if you are willing to hear them out and see the plan as it is unfolding in their mind, you quickly learn that most of the time they are just trying to communicate their larger vision of what is possible and show you potential where you haven't seen it before.

Imbalances of the Wood Element

When the Wood Element becomes imbalanced, the physical symptoms commonly experienced are insomnia – usually in the form of waking up in the middle of the night around 3 AM – as well as excessive dreaming or the absence of dreams. Digestive disturbances related to emotional upset or muscle tension and tightness, especially around the rib cage or diaphragm, may manifest. Other common symptoms include blurred vision, floaters, headaches, migraines, dry skin or brittle nails, and PMS.

Depression, moodiness, and erratic or repressed emotions can surface when the Wood Element is not properly supported. An individual may feel disorganized or even disorientated, experiencing vague anxieties. They can also become prone to outbursts of anger, letting their temper get the best of them. If the Wood Element is quite deficient, an individual may experience timidity or an inability to stand up for themselves.

Disconnected from their truth, they may feel as though they lack vision, causing them to wander aimlessly. In this uncommitted state, they tend to abandon anything at the first sight of an obstacle or hardship.[17]

Winning at Life

A Wood type's physicality is usually one of their strengths; they're typically quite wiry and lean, with a tendency to be athletic and excel at physical pursuits. These traits combined with their knack for working hard, goal setting, and pushing themselves toward excellence allow them to be quite accomplished in the activities and sports of their choosing. Wood types like to win. Who doesn't? But in a Wood's case, it's a whole other level. Their drive and determination to reach their potential and achieve their personal best are like no other.

This doesn't mean that Wood types are only capable of solo sports. This same drive allows them to be an excellent teammate, though it's likely that they will climb the ranks to team captain at some point. A Wood type is an excellent motivator, especially if surrounded by others who are eager to show up and compete with their best effort. After their time front and center on the court or field is finished, Wood types often find themselves on the sidelines, coaching and leading others.

As a Wood type ages, it's important for them to remain active even if there is no specific goal or incentive to train hard. Moving the Qi and getting the blood flowing through the muscles and the body ensures that they don't get tight and rigid. Such rigidity has the potential to not only affect the physical body, by creating stuck energy and pain, it also creates lethargy in the mind, clouding their vision and ability to make decisions and leaving them feeling lost without direction or purpose.

Organization and Planning

Similar to Metal types, most Woods like rules, structure and boundaries, which manifests in being exceptionally organized and regimented.

---

[17] Dechar, L. (2006). *Five spirits.* Lantern Books.

Making lists and plans allow them to implement and execute the vision they have. By breaking down the tasks required to accomplish their goals step by step, they can apply strategy and precision to ensure that there is a stable foundation to support their next move.

For a Wood type, being organized is critical to making decisions and assessing where they are on their journey. Many Woods will try to control every aspect of their routine and regimen to protect themselves from falling behind or feeling lost. Our culture glorifies self-control, which only fuels Wood's innate tendency to hold themselves accountable every moment of their day. This means they may never give themselves a pass or break from being the idealized version of themselves they have created.

If they are unable to access this level of perfection, a Wood type fears they will succumb to the chaos, lose control of the situation, and be unable to get ahead of it again. This can result in apathy and the loss of their innovative spark. To circumvent this fate, a Wood type may become hypervigilant and overly rigid about what they engage with and pursue.

When moments of feeling lost creep in, rather than immersing themselves in deep introspection to find answers or the next steady step, a Wood type will look outwardly to others for direction. They may hire coach after coach or jump between gurus, hoping that someone else can tell them what they need to do or how to be. In these moments, they may give up their autonomy to others to create the boundaries, structure, and possibly even identity they crave.

My Way or No Way

When it comes to assessing the effects of a Wood type's assertiveness and directness, there is a fine line between asset and liability. Wood types are particular, and they have strong opinions on what is the right and wrong way to do something. As I mentioned before, Woods like to be right, and therefore they usually consider their way the right – and only – way to perform a particular task or action. This obviously has the potential to create friction with other personalities who have strong opinions that differ from theirs.

Always perceiving their own ideas as the best can create a fixed mindset in Wood types, resulting in situations where they are unwilling to hear out alternative solutions or other points of view. This rigidity can endanger a project or relationship. When a Wood is unwilling to compromise, other Element types may be too intimidated to speak up and instead may do something not necessarily in their own best interest to make a Wood type happy. Being on the bad side of a Wood type isn't a fun time, given their potential for anger outbursts, moodiness, and irritability.

A Wood type can benefit from acknowledging this personality trait and reminding themselves that there is knowledge in the collective. Others have expertise, and by working together, it is possible to create something far greater than what a single person can conceive or execute. Also, it's important to remember that just because other people have alternative points of view or ideas based on their unique experience does not mean they are necessarily critical of a Wood type's direction or plans. The strongest trees are the ones flexible enough to bend in the wind. If everyone has the same goal, the ability to remain flexible will create the best solutions for all – not to mention a more pleasant culture in which to build and thrive.

And let's not forget that if, for some reason, a Wood type is experiencing self-doubt – perhaps due to a past event in which they were prevented from getting what they want – they may display the opposite characteristics. They can be indirect and unable to access their desires, let alone state them aloud to anybody else. Wood types in this state may display passive-aggressive tendencies and take out their frustration on others using an overly sarcastic, somewhat snarky sense of humor.

R-E-B-E-L

The rebellious streak embodied within a Wood type is twofold.

First, don't tell a Wood type what they can or can't do. You will be met with immediate pushback. In fact, they will stop at nothing to prove you wrong. Obstacles will be overcome regardless of the cost. For a Wood, the satisfaction of being righteous and victorious is entirely worth whatever sacrifice is required to get there.

Second, this rebel quality is further exacerbated by the fact that a Wood type isn't much of a fan of authority. The irony is, of course, that Wood types, with their gift for leadership, often find themselves in roles of authority within their professions. But while mostly they enjoy the benefits of structure and boundaries, they will at times find them constraining and feel compelled to push them away.

This is especially true if they view rules and structures, and the institutions that uphold them, to be out of date, unproductive, and unnecessary. In this case, they will rebel, protest, and make their opinions known to whomever will listen. If their objections fall on deaf ears, they will use their ingenuity to devise a better way, and begin making changes on their own.

A Wood's ability to organize isn't limited to making checklists and completing work on time. Naturally equipped with a barometer for BS and injustice, a Wood type may organize large-scale groups and initiatives to fight for voices that are marginalized and in need of allies.

Whether they're leading the charge or merely lending their voice to a cause, a Wood type feels the injustices of the world deeply and will look for ways to be part of the solution, channeling their frustrations and anger into something positive.

It's important for Woods to be aware that rebellion holds an escalating energy, and it can take on a life of its own. Wood types should constantly check in with their motivations and the reasons why they are choosing to push the boundaries. Are they rebelling for the sake of rebelling? Or are they rebelling with purpose – and will greater growth and development result from their nonconformity?

Don't You Dare Lie

Following truth is a core requirement for a Wood type. This requirement will be interpreted and met in different ways by individual Wood types, but one way it often shows up is in a desire to be told the truth and have others be true to their word.

I joke with some of my Wood clients that if I were to ever lie, or not follow through on something I said, I would be dead to them. They laugh because in context it feels crazy that I would ever put myself in that position. Hello, I'm an Earth dominant. But every one of them agrees. Yes, if I failed to follow through or stay true to my word, our professional relationship would be over. It would be nearly impossible to earn their trust back. No one wants to be lied to or let down, but especially not a Wood. When betrayed in this way, a Wood type's response is immediate and far-reaching. They lose trust right then and there, and waste no time chopping the offender out of the picture for good.

Wood types don't give you second chances to prove yourself and win back their trust. You get one. But if, somehow, they allow you a shot at regaining their faith and trust, be aware that it will be a long process with many tests and hurdles. And if you fail, know that Woods can hold a grudge until the end of time.

Learn to Rest, Not to Quit

Woods work until the job is done. Much like Metal types, Woods are able to assess a project and break it down into components that can be delegated and brought to completion. The difference between a Metal and a Wood is that while Metals are focused on the process and doing a proficient job (knowing that this will lead to a completed and well-done project), Woods care more about the end result and getting the project finished so they can move on to the next one. This is not to say that Woods don't also want to do a quality job. However, for Woods, vision is everything. They will continue to push and drive the project ahead toward the vision or goal they have set for themselves.

It is wise for a Wood to make note of their tendency for tunnel vision, especially when it makes them unwilling to open their eyes to other possibilities. Flexibility can offer its own efficiencies to a project, possibly even allowing one's vision for the project and end goal to expand.

Wood types may also find it helpful to remember that it's okay to rest. Taking a step back from immediate pressures and tasks allows one to see the larger picture. It also helps rejuvenate the body after intense effort. Wood types tend to burn the candle at both ends and only rest when they are physically unable to do anything else. But being burned out and stressed are not good looks on anyone. Woods may benefit from remembering that it is not necessary to run themselves ragged or wait until they are unwell to take a break. Their vision or momentum will not escape or leave if they get a solid night's sleep, have a few days off, or even lengthen self-imposed timelines.

Comparison of Woods and Metals

You will see that I've made a few comparisons between Wood types and Metal types in this chapter. There's good reason for that. In a lot of ways, Wood and Metal types are extremely similar. Sometimes even I have trouble discerning whether a person is one or the other. For this reason, I feel it's important to list some of the subtle differences between them, so you can better understand how both types resonate within you and your Alchemy.

To discern which Element is being represented, I find it helpful to first consider their different energetics. Metal is more yin, more collected and reserved, whereas Wood is more yang – expansive, loud, forward, and at times audacious.

As previously discussed, both like organization, systems, and bringing a job to completion. But while the end result may be the same, how they get there is different. A Metal type prefers order and ensuring that the work is done properly. They want to be able to stand behind it after the fact. A Wood type wants the job done NOW – yesterday was actually preferable, but the current moment will suffice. While they also want the job done well, they are less concerned with the details or process; more often than not, this one project is merely a piece of their greater vision. Pressing forward to the next job or phase is equally as valuable to them.

Another defining difference is that a Wood can't sit still. They feel compelled to always be doing something. Their minds are constantly on the future – and the tasks, plans and directions they will pursue. As I mentioned earlier, they will only rest when they have no choice – their bodies have given out or someone has forced them to. A Metal doesn't have this issue. The energetic of Metal brings one to the space between, to the here and now. This quality helps Metals find satisfaction within the current moment. They don't always need to prove themselves or their agenda.

When stressed, a Wood type, who often falls into the workaholic category, may try to take back all the responsibilities and do everything themselves. This usually results in them being incredibly angry, bitter, and resentful of everyone else's incompetence, only fueling their rationale as to why they can't delegate the work that needs doing. On the other hand, a Metal under stress will revert to old patterns or systems that may not be helpful in the present circumstance. It's as if they get stuck in a loop, doing more of what isn't working. If they could step back and get a different perspective, they might see other options or methods that would be more helpful to them.

Within relationships, both Elements are incredibly kind, generous, and loyal. They would walk to the ends of the earth for you, although this quality is often hidden until you get to know them. They don't smother you with love and kindness like Earths and Fires, but make no mistake, Woods and Metals will show up for you if the relationship has been built on mutual trust and friendship.

When something within the relationship is off, you will know. A Metal will often detach, cutting themselves off from the situation. They may come across as cold or unfeeling. This is how they ensure they don't say something they don't mean. They avoid confrontation and any drama that may result by being unavailable to it. A Wood Element is the complete opposite. They need to express themselves and have no issues with showing their feelings. They also love a good argument. However, if their feelings and comments are ignored or they have been lied to, they will end a relationship, FOREVER. Remember I mentioned their ability to hold a grudge. You might as well be dead, because to them you've stopped existing.

Healing Tools for Your Inner Wood

Move Some Qi: The Wood type requires adequate movement of their body, or they risk getting stagnant and inflexible. Any form of movement works to accomplish this. Choose something that gets your heart rate going, encourages a sweat, and warms your muscles. See how you feel afterwards. So many variables come into play with exercise and movement; it's important to honor what your body needs on a daily basis. As a Wood type, you may rely on your athleticism and push yourself to the point of injury. Be aware of your limits.

Vision Boards and Imagination: Wood types are especially receptive to working with their active imagination. Take the time to paint pictures of your dreams and fantasies. This will help to re-engage the Wood Element to guide your mind toward your goals and the bigger WHY.

Express Your Inner Frustrations: The emotion of the Wood Element is anger. It is necessary to express your frustrations and let them out in a constructive manner. Actively engaging your anger can connect you to your truth and clear obstacles on the path to your desires. Remember, the inverse of anger is power.

Delight in the Beauty of Nature: Spring is the season associated with the Wood Element. Connecting with nature's beauty and emergence is necessary for a Wood type. Allow yourself to be in awe of the life force that surrounds you: feel the breeze; feast your eyes on the colors and movements of the trees. Listen to the birdsong and let it soothe your nervous system. Set aside a day to observe and become aware of growth and beauty to help inspire your next course of action and greater vision.[18]

---

[18] Dechar, L. (2006). *Five spirits.* Lantern Books.

Innate Strengths of a Wood Type

- Natural-born leader
- A capacity to strategize and execute a vision to completion
- Prioritizes growth and development
- Passionate about "causes," justice and fairness; stands up for others
- Warrior energy embodied
- Generally positive and upbeat
- Constantly seeks improvement – willing to think outside the box to pioneer a new way

Opportunities for Growth for a Wood Type

- Can get hung up on hierarchy, structure, and rules
- Assertive behavior that can become overzealous and aggressive when left unchecked
- Rebellious behavior – particularly when younger
- "My way or the highway" – a tendency for tunnel vision; unwilling to see other perspectives
- Can be indecisive at times
- Quick to anger; often experiences low-level frustration[19]

[19] Hicks, A., & Hicks, J. (1999). *Healing your emotions.* Thorsons.

Chapter 6

The Fire Type

Lover — Performer — Connector

The emotion associated most closely with the Fire type is joy. Want to identify the Fire types in your life? Look for the group enthralled with laughter at your next function and see who has everyone in stitches. Fire types are joyful, lively and incredibly funny. Laughter and a good time are usually to be had when a Fire is in the room.

A Fire type embodies the Fire Element in its many forms. The bright light. The flames that can be tamed and controlled or left to burn out of control. The sparks with all their wildness and potential. The ash that dissipates and floats away in the wind. The slow-burning embers that smolder into the night.

A Fire type is open and available to adventure, welcoming any opportunities that come their way – the more fun, spontaneous, or random, the better, as it increases the likelihood of a wild story that can be shared and laughed about later. They are charismatic communicators who can literally make friends with just about everyone, even the person in front of them in line at the coffee shop.

Their fiery personality leads them to be incredibly passionate about whatever they are currently immersed in, whether it's a person, conversation, project, or study. If it piques their interest, they can become completely enthralled – until suddenly, they're not. At which point they will drop it completely. Being on the receiving end of their attention can be all-consuming, and their disinterest may seem to come completely out of nowhere. But Fire types tend to run a bit hot and cold: completely in at one point and then completely out the next, without caring or needing to ever return to a passion again.

One way you can begin to pick out Fire types (or people with Fire as a strong secondary Element) in your life is through deep listening. Fires are said to have a laughing sound in their voice. Personally, I find that they tend to laugh and talk at the same time in their conversations. They also like to talk, so you have ample opportunity to listen for it. Fires often talk very fast, so fast that at times their words get muddled. Their brains move even faster than their mouths, sometimes making what they're saying unclear. It's not uncommon for their stories to jump between multiple timelines or for them to get distracted by a tangent. But somehow, most of the time, it all blends together and makes sense at the end.

This is partly because a Fire's thought patterns and ways of seeing the world aren't as linear as some of the other types. Please trust me when I say this. It's not wrong. If you are a Fire type, YOU ARE NOT WRONG. Fire types lead with their hearts, and the heart feels and acts in directions and ways that are mysterious and wonderful. It's okay. In fact, it's miraculous, and the more you're able to bestow compassion on yourself and your ways of being, the greater your ability to trust your heart and inner knowing, which will strengthen and lead you to greater opportunity.

Fires can sometimes have a reputation for being flaky. This is because a Fire can become confused or frustrated when attempting to follow other people's plans or expectations. If they feel that the course of action is outdated or restrictive, they will simply abandon it. This is in part because the energetic of Fire is fast moving. What was true one day may not be true for them the next. If given the autonomy to speak up and share their knowledge and truth of the moment, a Fire type can dispel this perception of being flaky and constantly changing their mind and direction, and instead be recognized for their gifts. One of those gifts is the ability to connect to the heartbeat of a moment and allow love to guide them through it. This makes them strong catalysts for change and evolution.

With the ability to command an audience and the charisma to get others to listen to what they have to say, a Fire type can be empowered to take center stage and impart sparks of truth that cause others to wake up and invite their own inner light to shine forth.

Convening with their soul and the parts of themselves they feel insecure about can be scary for Fires. They have great depths, but they may fear that self-inquiry or allowing themselves to feel sadness may consume them. They worry about being unable to come back to being their happy self. For this reason, they tend to not want to spend much time in deep contemplation or reflection. They would sooner life be easy, happy, and positive. Too much time spent looking at hurt can feel like a slippery slope into despair and heartbreak, and who wants that? Instead, Fire types prefer to live in the moment and try to not worry about what tomorrow or the future might bring.

This fear of being alone with their thoughts and feelings can motivate a Fire to not want to be alone most of the time. This may manifest as anxiety or a fear of missing out (FOMO). Fires seek people and community to potentially distract them from their inner monologue. If successful, they will likely find themselves the life of the party, seeking adoration to counteract their insecurities. Moving from one person or relationship to the next prevents them from having to go home to be with themselves.

Lastly, Fire types are huggers, craving personal touch and affection. They prefer relationships in which they are free to express their affection and adoration for the other person. This is in part to fulfill their core requirements of seeking closeness and experiencing love and affection. Public displays of affection are welcome. However, when a Fire is imbalanced and they are overcompensating to fulfill this requirement, they can easily become overly clingy or needy and unable to recognize their personal autonomy or that of the other person.

Imbalances of the Fire Element

If the Fire Element is in disharmony, common physical symptoms that will manifest are insomnia (usually experienced as a busy mind that is unable to fall asleep), anxiety, palpitations, panic attacks, an inability to concentrate, and a tendency to be easily startled. One may become even more talkative than normal, and tend toward mania, hyperactivity, or restlessness. Breathlessness, daytime sweating, and stuffiness or pain in the heart region can also result. Believe it or not, extreme timidity may ensue if a Fire hasn't been able to express their authentic self for some time.

One psychological-spiritual manifestation that is common when the Fire Element is imbalanced is feeling a lack of coherence, where one's personality doesn't fit the life one is living. Without the internal flame burning, a person can feel as though they lack inspiration and insight into what their life and purpose are meant to be. Fire types can struggle to perceive their uniqueness when their innate fire has been tamed or reined in by others. A Fire type can find themselves questioning what is truly "right for me," and despairing that things have never been quite right. If it's always been wrong before, why would it suddenly be right now?[20]

Happy, Happy

A Fire type is generally a shining light in the room, with an infectious laugh and the ability to instantly lift the mood and bring joy to everyone around them. This is almost unconscious to them; it's simply part of their nature. Being sensitive to the energy of their environment and others in their company, they will be uncomfortable when someone is feeling down and feel a personal responsibility to find a way to cheer them up.

But this superpower has a shadow. Because they can affect other people's moods so easily and change them, it's not uncommon for a Fire to misinterpret the reason someone might be unhappy and take it personally. Being center stage for many of their social encounters makes them vulnerable to believing everything is about them. They then

---

[20] Dechar, L. (2006). *Five spirits.* Lantern Books.

proceed to blame themselves or feel slighted if their attempts to help don't work or are ignored. It's as if they momentarily forget that people have stories, beliefs and lives that exist without them.

To avoid this confusion, it is helpful for a Fire type to develop their skills of discernment and personal boundaries. This will help them stay centered amidst the swirl of emotions they may encounter on any given day. Fires benefit from asking themselves: What is in my control? In what ways do I seek to alter the mood of a room or discussion? What is my motivation in needing to change how someone feels? Is it possible that I don't know the whole story?

Over time these questions will assist them in realizing where the line lies between wanting to support and serve others, and what is not their responsibility and none of their business.

Comedy and Performance

From a very early age most Fires learn that they can command an audience. They're charismatic and magnetic, which make others gravitate to them. Being in front of others, whether on a stage, in a boardroom, or at the center of a party, comes naturally to them. It's not uncommon for many actors and comedians to have Fire dominating their chart. Humor and clowning serve a variety of purposes. First, being funny, even if it's self-deprecating humor, diffuses the mood and lifts up the energy of the room. Second, it brings people's attention back to them as the center of the conversation. Last, it helps them to deflect or hide their insecurities from others and sometimes themselves.

Fires often figure that if they're busy making everyone else happy, then maybe they can be happy too. Perhaps they can accumulate enough evidence to allow themselves to believe that they are loveable and worthy of love. If everyone is smiling and having a good time, then they must be doing something right. This love and adoration can distract from any feelings of melancholy or sadness that they're trying to escape, ignore or cover up.

If you're a Fire type, I implore you to find individuals for whom you don't have to perform or provide entertainment all the time, if ever. To have safe relationships where you can rest this reflex and show up as yourself is so important. You are worthy of love. Period. There is nothing you need to do to earn it. If you are not a Fire type but have identified Fire types in your close circle, I encourage you to notice when they're using positivity and humor to mask hurt. In between the jokes and laughing, take a moment to step back and notice your friend, beyond how they're making you feel. There's a popular saying, "Check in on your strong friend"; I would add that you should check in on your funny friends, too.

Constantly concerned with the external expressions of themselves and others, Fire types may end up ignoring their internal landscapes and the gifts that self-awareness can grant them. Being able to unhook from the external gratification and adoration that comes from constantly performing can provide Fire types with an opportunity to gain autonomy and decide how they show up in any given moment.

Bringing the fire and excitement to every situation can be taken advantage of by others. This can lead a Fire type to become resentful and annoyed at everyone. It can make them feel that they are only considered "the entertainment" and not someone of substance. It taints the love and adoration that they feel when included, because it starts to seem fake or circumstantial, based on them doing their shtick. This can create burnout and cause Fires to end relationships, the only way they can see to release themselves from the social contract that has been created.

An Open Book

A Fire type's big, open heart allows them to create connection and vulnerability with almost anyone. Being in a Fire's presence causes most people to relax, let down their walls, and find shared interests. Sharing freely with others comes easily to a Fire; however, it can make for messy situations at times. This is particularly true if a Fire has trouble discerning what's appropriate to share and what's best saved for a more intimate setting with trusted individuals. It's very easy for a Fire type to get swept up in the moment and share too much, revealing their innermost secrets and vulnerabilities to a room full of strangers or someone they barely know.

This can also manifest in rushing ahead and skipping the foundational steps of relationship building with others. For example, they may fall in love very quickly, allowing passion, lust, and the yearning for connection to fuel a new relationship beyond a more natural unfolding. This of course sometimes works out amazingly well, but often it results in not noticing red flags, such as the other person being unavailable or unable to reciprocate the same intensity of love.

When someone doesn't reflect back the same vulnerability and connection, a Fire type can internalize this as rejection and a confirmation of their deepest insecurity, that they aren't loveable. Of course, the far likelier explanation is that others have different core requirements, and the need to connect may be less important to them or manifest differently. Nevertheless, this misunderstanding can result in Fires becoming uncertain of how to create a relationship that allows them to show up as themselves. They want to be open but are fearful that doing so will make them appear too needy and ultimately leave them all alone.

Dampening the Flame – Isolating/Rebuffing Rejection

A Fire type who has had their heart broken may try to wall up and protect themselves in hopes of mitigating future loss and hurt. In some capacity, we all do this with the end of a relationship. We learn new information about ourselves and what we are willing to be open to, then we put protections in place to ensure we receive the respect, love, and commitment we're looking for the next time.

For a Fire type, discerning when to open up and when to close down can be a bit muddled. They prefer to be either wide open and available, or closed shut. Occupying the gray space in between, where they remain open while putting some guards and protections in place, can feel to them as if they are withholding their heart, love, and authentic self.

When hurt, Fires can resort to extreme protectionism. They will close themselves off from others by becoming incredibly introverted and unsocial. This can be brought on by incredible sadness: think of those moments when you're halfway through a pint of Ben & Jerry's and you proclaim that you'll never date again. I joke, but for Fires, potential rejection or betrayal is not a joke. Fires may remove themselves from all social situations that may tempt them to open up and let someone into their fragile heart.

With practice, a Fire type can become quite cunning in making everyone believe that they are open, friendly, and easy to be around, when on the inside they are walled up and unwilling to have conversations and relationships that go beyond the superficial "light and airy" level. To an outsider, it may appear that this person is loved and surrounded by tons of amazing friends; the truth may be that they have no deep relationships, only acquaintances or brief hook-ups.

Face Time Is Non-Negotiable

I cannot express just how important it is for a Fire type to engage in one-to-one deep conversations.

Fire types need face time, daily if possible, where they can be seen by and see another person. Engaging in conversation about something real allows them to feel whole. But be forewarned, Fire types don't do quick chit-chat coffee dates. No, these are events, sometimes hours long. The poor person sitting beside them at the coffee shop may end up incredibly uncomfortable after overhearing the conversation. Nothing is off limits, and the discussion may span a multitude of topics and directions.

Without this type of engagement, Fires will be constantly searching and seeking more connections, always networking and putting themselves out there to try to find this type of meaningful, grounding, and fulfilling interaction. On the extreme end of this search for proximity and connection, a Fire type may adopt more promiscuous behavior to satisfy their present needs over establishing long-term commitments.

If they're unable to join already established groups, Fires will create their own, calling on the vast number of connections they have. They may even invite someone they met on the way to the event. Fire types have a knack for creating community and connecting people who have common interests, but it's important for a Fire to not always be the one creating the sparks. This responsibility can make them feel frenetic and easily lead to burnout. To counterbalance, Fires require supportive relationships that allow them to show up however they need to in each moment.

Because they can draw people in and make them feel comfortable, Fire types are often in professions where connection is important, for example, coaching, counseling, or other jobs involving one-on-one intensive work or workshops.

All Work and No Play Makes for a Very Dull Flame

Western culture is built on the belief that we have to work first and play later. No playing until your homework is done. Work your ass off all week, so you can enjoy your weekend or the vacation that comes around once or twice a year. Focus and you will be rewarded. This mode of being really doesn't serve a Fire type in any way. It doesn't fit with their creativity, gifts, and flow. Actually, it doesn't serve any type, but a Fire often internalizes the poor fit to mean that their natural flow and rhythm are wrong. That they are wrong. This couldn't be further from the truth. A Fire type needs to play and experience pleasure daily. If it's absent, they will bore easily and begin to shut down. Connecting to their joy and allowing themselves pleasure spark a Fire type's desires and creative potential.

This is why it's important for them to experiment with their workday and preferred flow. If you have Fire in your Alchemy, ask yourself how you can break up your work hours with intermittent moments of play. A quick dance party in the office with the door closed? Sneaking out for a long lunch or reading a chapter of erotic fiction between tasks? It doesn't matter what you do, as long as it brings you joy.

Do It Your Way

From a non-Fire perspective, a Fire's approach to projects and work may look a little disjointed, but it works for them – and it's not wrong. Fires provide sparks of inspiration; they infuse projects with fun and play, and they bring an almost whimsical curiosity to their work that allows them to listen to their heart and spirit. They may start in one place and end up somewhere totally different. It may not be linear, and it's not meant to be.

Fires also bring passion to a project. Like an intense all-consuming bonfire, they may burn through ideas and inspiration as they drill down to the heart of the matter. But when a Fire is ready to let go of a project, particularly one that has consumed their energies, it's as if a switch is flipped and the flames die. At that point, Fires will retreat to collect or conserve their resources, and wait and see where their next inspiration leads.

To non-Fires, it can appear as if their Fire colleagues are always frenetically going off on tangents and never know where they're heading next. But this is how Fires take in information. It's wise for a Fire type to embrace this quality in themselves, as it will support them in discerning and identifying what qualifies for their attention and what doesn't. This will result in them engaging in more activities and projects that light them up, optimize their creative potential, and bring them joy. However, a Fire type would do well to remember to take care of themselves while in the throes of inspiration or passion, as they tend to forget that their energy and enthusiasm must be supported by their body. A solid self-care regimen can go a long way to holding space for their core requirements, which we'll uncover shortly, and creates a foundation for trusting their own way, especially when it is different from everyone else's.

The Fire–Water Connection: When One Feels Like a Walking Contradiction

Among my clients, an interesting Elemental Alchemy is common: Fire dominant with Water secondary, or the opposite: Water dominant with Fire secondary. This combination can be at times confusing to navigate. Most individuals I've worked with who identify with this combination describe feeling like they are pulled in two opposite directions. They feel like a walking contradiction. The truth is, they are, and the sooner they can embrace this fact the easier it will be for them to get to the heart of what is holding them back from creating a life that they love.

Being a Fire–Water combo, with either Element dominant, means that energetically you oscillate between two Elements at the opposite ends of the circle: at the top, the highest-yang, fast-moving energetic of Fire, and at the bottom, the most yin, still, and dense energetic of Water. We haven't explored core requirements yet, but I'm sure it won't come as a surprise that the requirements of these Elements can conflict – the Fire within seeking spontaneity, connection, intimacy and closeness, while the Water wants to feel safe and secure while experiencing freedom and lots of alone time. This dichotomy can create a lot of conflicting messages for individuals: they want to be alone to relax and recharge, and at the same time, they don't want to miss out on opportunities to play, have crazy fun, and be the star of the show.

Often there is an underlying feeling that one must choose to be one or the other. But it is actually important that both energetics are given time and space to be intentionally felt and embodied. Your inner Fire needs adequate time with other people, socializing, collaborating, and exercising your star power. Your inner Water requires you to trust your inclination to come inward and spend time alone, consolidating your resources and enhancing your intuitive abilities so you can forge your own path. Too much time in Fire and you will dry up the well and be vulnerable to burnout, unable to access the depth of your soul. Too much Water and you will douse your flame and fizzle your enthusiasm and natural curiosity.

To help mediate these tendencies, such individuals might try cultivating a bit of the Earth Element to act as a pivot to support holding both energetics in right relationship. This doesn't mean taking on another personality. Reading over the Earth type chapter may help you to acknowledge how Earth supports you already. You may also identify individuals in your life that exemplify Earth qualities who you can lean on as you create greater supports for yourself. I would also like to invite you to spend time with the upcoming chapter "Earth: Self-Love & Caretaking" as this will provide a wealth of information to assist you in cultivating the appropriate support to allow both the Fire and Water parts of yourself to thrive.

Healing Tools for Your Inner Fire

Create a Happy List: Make a list of activities that bring you joy and make you feel happy. Come up with at least 20 items and keep going if you can think of more. Keep it where you can see it daily and choose to schedule at least one item (more is better) per day. Weaving happiness, joy and pleasure into your day keeps your Fire alive, allowing greater sparks of desire to come into awareness.

Closeness and Physical Touch: According to family therapist Virginia Satir, "We need 4 hugs a day for survival. We need 8 hugs a day for maintenance. We need 12 hugs a day for growth." Other types might be a bit squeamish about this statement, but for a Fire type, this is truth. Physical connection and closeness are necessary. It's okay to be the hugger in your group of friends or want to hold your partner's hand when you walk down the street. Identify the ways you need physical affection in your relationships and ask for them.

Celebration and Connection: Friendship, sisterhood/brotherhood, and community are incredibly important for Fire types. You are a natural connector and collaborator. Embrace this aspect of yourself and make room in your social calendar to engage, play, laugh and love. These aren't frivolous events in your schedule; they are necessary. You need to speak or engage with another human being in a meaningful way every single day.

Self-Love: Loving yourself is the truest expression of love you can feel. Daily devotions of self-love strengthen the belief that you are loveable. They will heal your heart however it needs to be healed in the moment. Take time to delight in yourself, and self-care through daily acts of kindness to yourself.

Laugh Daily: Laughter is the gateway to experiencing the highest vibration in the body and creates lasting effects on the body, mind and soul as you relate to the world.

Innate Strengths of a Fire Type

- A natural ability to bring fun, joy and laughter to any situation
- A capacity to create intimacy and connection with others
- Finds the silver lining and remains optimistic in trying circumstances
- Leads by inspiring others with enthusiasm and charisma
- A natural-born performer, able to command a room with ease
- Willing to be vulnerable in front of others

Opportunities for Growth for a Fire Type

- Overly sensitive; can be superficial and struggle to experience deeper intimacy
- Can be overly dramatic and experience fluctuating emotions
- Can become clingy and insecure when in unsupportive relationships
- A tendency to force intimacy by relating inappropriately or abandoning boundaries
- Can believe that every situation or conversation is about them
- Overly concerned with what others think of them – forgets to go inwards for appreciation & acceptance[21]

---

[21] Hicks, A., & Hicks, J. (1999). *Healing your emotions.* Thorsons.

Chapter 7

The Core Requirements

The Core Requirements of Your 5 Element Type

Now that you're aware of your unique 5 Element Alchemy and some key characteristics of each Element type, you're ready to start calling upon this knowledge and applying it in your day-to-day life. But to get the most out of what you've learned, there is one more important piece of the puzzle: the core requirements.

The core requirements of your unique Element Alchemy describe how and why you engage with the world as you do. They hold the keys to understanding your relationships and how you choose to show up. These are your motivators; they have the capacity to bring out the very best in you – and sometimes the worst. They are what drive you to seek change or to shy away from it. They are your "why."

Your core requirements serve as your navigation system, your medicine, and your saboteur, all at once. They are constantly seeking embodiment so that you can feel whole. If you consciously engage with them, your core requirements can act as a guide and friend, providing opportunities for self-inquiry and helping you choose specific actions and relationships to bring you closer to the life that you envision for yourself. However, if you're not engaging with them in this way, you are still engaging with them – unconsciously. If this is the case, they're driving the ship and seeking satisfaction and fulfillment on their own terms. The unconscious doesn't distinguish between healthy and unhealthy habits and behaviors. It will try to meet your requirements in whatever way it can, deal with the fallout, and then try to reconcile the requirements again. This is why one's quirks, habits and traits surface as they do.

In moments of uncertainty, do you find yourself second-guessing your intuition or looking to the next book or guru to give you answers? When the high of listening to your favorite self-help speakers dissipates, do you feel frustrated and like something is still missing? There's a reason for that. The answer isn't more ideas or tools. Everything you need lies here within your core requirements.[22]

How Your Core Requirements Work

Each Element has particular needs that must be reconciled to feel whole and generate the next phase of growth. A seed doesn't just lay there and will itself to become a flower; it requires soil, nutrients, sunshine, water, love, and tending to grow and thrive. As individuals, we too require certain conditions and supports to evolve and blossom. Our individual Alchemies provide the road map to understanding these requirements.

If you're hoping for a cookie-cutter model or a list of five things we can all do to achieve wholeness, prepare to be disappointed. I think we're way past believing that healing and wholeness can be accomplished with a 10-step plan. Every person has their own path. The good news is your Alchemy will guide you and ensure your inner wisdom prevails.

Depending on your unique Element Alchemy, some requirements are going to feel easier to reconcile than others. The more prevalent an Element is in your chart, the more often you will be negotiating and reassessing how its requirements are being met. Some may at times feel elusive and hard to embody, while others come through with the utmost ease.

---

[22] Core requirements are inspired by Angela and John Hicks's work on big issues and unanswered questions for each Element type, in combination with my clinical experience (see Hicks, A., & Hicks, J. (1999). *Healing your emotions.* Thorsens).

With time and attention, you will learn to engage with the requirements of each of the 5 Elements, regardless of how much they show up in your chart. Remember that each Element contains medicine that will reveal itself depending on your life's circumstances. When you need it, it will show up and invite you to cultivate more of its virtues and do the self-work needed to heal.

It's also important to acknowledge when you are struggling with particular core requirements. You may need to make choices and changes to ensure these requirements are met. This may require difficult conversations with your family or circle of influence. The good news is that through this process you will find your next steady steps. And as you do them, your world will shift, and new confidence and beliefs will empower you to move forward in the direction of your heart, fully embodied as you.

The Core Requirements – The Big Picture

The following chart can be used to notice the overall ebb and flow of each Element's requirements as they relate to your current life circumstances. Take note of which requirements you feel are embodied and attended to, as well as those that you feel are not currently satisfied. This awareness will allow you to gain greater clarity around which Elements' requirements are feeling supported and which you may wish to spend more time cultivating.

The goal, however, is not necessarily to have each and every requirement fully embodied or satisfied 100 percent of the time. The purpose is to give you a point of reference of the areas of focus and alignment that are occurring in your life at this moment.

Regardless of where you would like to go with this journey, start with where you're at now. Use the inclinations of your soul that surface today to lead. There is medicine here for you to experience. Embrace the fact that this is not a race. There are no awards for a "right and perfect" answer. Trust your real answers; they invite you to go deeper, calling you closer to your soul and inner wisdom.

To gain more insight into your chart, you may wish to try the additional exercises available for download in the bonus section: www.ashleyabbs.com/5elementalchemy-resources.

Now, we will dive deeper into the requirements of each Element. Use the questions provided to further uncover the unique requirements of your Element Alchemy and your relationship to them. You may find it helpful to journal using the questions as writing prompts, or to bring a specific question into your meditation or to discuss with a friend.

Core Requirements of Earth

The Earth Element reinforces your capacity to trust that you are enough. It invites you to come home to yourself and satisfy your physical, mental and emotional needs, so that you can then contribute to the well-being of your relationships and wider community.

The core requirements of the Earth Element help to orient you at the center of your own life by acknowledging how you best feel supported, nourished and grounded. They recognize the importance of having the mental clarity to understand when you are aligned to your true potential and authentic expression.

Feeling Supported:

Everyone wants someone in their corner – a spouse, partner, friend – who is there in both the good and the not-so-great times of life. Earth types often act as this support system for everyone else; however, it's important for them to recognize that they need support, too. They shouldn't have to shoulder everything on their own. Identifying how they want to be supported by others, as well as how they wish to support themselves, allows them to articulate their expectations and cultivate greater trust in the capabilities of others.

What does being supported by other people look like? What do you want to hear from them or have them do?

How do you support yourself when external affirmation isn't possible?

What does it feel like in your body when you're being supported?

What do you need to be and feel supported?

Being Nourished:

Being nourished is about more than just the food you eat. Nourishment is everything that you consume, from your environment to the words you read, hear, and repeat, the activities you engage in, and the people you fill your life with. The satisfaction you feel when properly nourished consolidates your knowing that you have and are enough. By broadening their definition of what nourishment means, Earth types can create healthier relationships to both themselves and their wider world. They may find they can reconcile this requirement with greater ease and in new ways.

What is your individual definition of nourishment?

What does it feel like when you are nourished?

What do you need to be and feel nourished?

Being Grounded:
Being grounded allows you to center your body, mind, and emotions amidst life's busyness. In this way, you stay in integrity with your soul and its expression. Earth types, with their tendency to get stuck in the idea phase, have difficulty actualizing their desires. By devoting energy to bringing ideas and thoughts down into their body, they will find it easier to follow through on their intentions, benefiting others as well as themselves.

What does it feel like in your body when you're grounded?

What does it feel like in your body when you're un-grounded?

What actions or tools assist you in coming back to your center and feeling grounded?

What is your relationship to ideas and follow-through? If it's a struggle, what supports do you feel would be helpful?

What in your life provides stabilizing energy that helps you to remain grounded?

Having Mental Clarity:
A clear mind provides the opportunity to connect to your potential and allow your soul to lead. Overthinking and worry will muddy the waters and create overwhelm. Earth types, as a result of taking on too much and being overburdened by worry and obligation, can struggle with mental bandwidth. This can leave them unable to prioritize their thoughts and needs; the noise is just too great. Acknowledging this aspect of themselves and creating tools to help them organize their thoughts and settle their worries allow inspiration and the whispers of their hearts to surface.

at does having mental clarity mean to you?

hat does it feel like when you experience mental clarity?

What practices or tools help you worry less, avoid overwhelm, and feel clearer more often?

Being Understood:

To be understood by others, you must first understand yourself. Knowing who you are and what you're about is the foundation to creating a life that you love and being in right relationship with other people. Earthy types who have got caught up in people-pleasing roles can lose connection to who they are and what they're about, because they are always becoming whomever they perceive others want them to be in order to create harmony. Becoming intimate with their own essence and understanding themselves without agenda enable them to be their own authority and live a life by their own design.

What does being understood mean to you?

At your core, who are you?

What's important to you?

How do you share and articulate this part of yourself to other people in your life?

Core Requirements of Metal

The Metal Element's core requirements center on the theme of consolidating worthiness. In particular, they focus on how you seek affirmation that you are worthy of your current life as well as the one that you desire.

These requirements include navigating the desire to be recognized; seeking completion; feeling adequate in what you do; and being deeply connected to your purpose. By meeting these requirements, you can find right relationship both internally – in how you perceive your lived experience and acquire self-confidence

– and externally – in the ways you wish to be acknowledged and affirmed in your work and relationships.

Receiving Recognition:

That inner-perfectionist type-A aspect of yourself wants to excel and be acknowledged for your efforts. However, largely this type of external validation is out of your control. This is why it's so important for Metal types in particular to discover ways to recognize and validate their own worthiness. Cultivating appreciation for their accomplishments and lived experience, in the quietness of their minds, can carry more weight than the opinions of others. This will also help them discern what type of recognition they want to receive from others and allow them to articulate it.

How and for what do you wish to be recognized?

How are you currently recognized, or how do you wish to seek recognition from others?

What is motivating your need to be recognized in these ways?

How do you recognize yourself, your gifts, and all that you are in this present moment?

Feeling Complete:

In the generation cycle of the Elements,[23] Metal is usually considered the end point. It's the place where the leaves turn to brown and fall from the

---

[23] The generation cycle or Sheng Cycle describes the sequencing of Elements, where each Element is generated by the one before, similar to the changing of seasons. Just as spring follows winter, Water generates Wood, Wood generates Fire, Fire generates Earth, Earth generates Metal, and Metal generates Water. This is sometimes expressed using the terms mother and child – for example, Metal is the child of Earth and the mother of Water (Maciocia, G. (1989). *The foundations of Chinese medicine.* Edinburgh: Churchill Livingstone).

tree; where one cycle ends, and another begins. Metal is where we find ourselves when something – a belief, pattern, way of being – needs to be refined and alchemized into something new. It is where we bring closure to what was so that new life can abound. Metal types seek completion by way of closure and natural endings to help tie up loose ends before they move on to something new.

What does completion feel like within your body and mind?

What in your current circumstance needs to be finished or brought to a close? How?

What in you requires closure or completion to move on to the next thing?

Feeling Adequate:

Your inner Metal motivates you to be competent and proficient at the tasks or work you do. However, your inner perfectionist may be digging in its heels and insisting on more than what's really required. This is why it's important to acknowledge what you actually need to do in order to feel adequate. Metal types often exceed what's necessary. It may be helpful to recognize just how far past they are pushing themselves and to question whether this is impeding their ability to move on to the next stage or step.

What does being adequate mean to you?

What do you need in order to feel adequate?

What does it feel like when you feel adequate?

How often do you surpass your own definition of adequacy?

Was it needed? Was it ultimately helpful?

Having Purpose:

Without purpose, what are we even doing here? For a Metal type to fully engage in a project, relationship, or cause, they have to feel that there is purpose and meaning behind it. This provides them with the resilience and tenacity to keep putting one foot in front of the other, even when they experience difficulty. After all, why continue to the next step without a reason for doing so?

What is your purpose? What is your "why"?

How do you live out your purpose in your daily life?

Where is your purpose reflected back to you in your work and relationships?

What does it feel like in your body when you are engaged with your purpose and implementing it in your work and relationships?

Core Requirements of Water

The Water Element and its core requirements center around safety, authenticity, and freedom. In particular, they focus on what is required to get ready to leap toward your dreams, and ultimately your destiny, even when you aren't sure yet where you will land.

Reconciling the core requirements of Water help you access the power of momentum and inertia. These requirements also recognize that to have faith in yourself and your decisions, it is essential to feel safe, secure, and able to mediate risks. Finally, they acknowledge that tapping into your authentic expression and experiencing freedom provide the necessary nuance to discern what opportunities and choices are the best fit for your individual path.

Feeling Safe:

Safety encompasses both emotional and physical protection against unknown and unintentional threats. Often it refers to what an individual needs in order to know that they will be okay in a given moment. For Water types, identifying what they need with regard to their safety helps them navigate their fear and come home to their intuition so they can trust themselves and their decisions.

What do you require to feel safe emotionally?

What do you require to feel safe physically?

What does it feel like in your body when you feel safe?

What do you require right now to feel safe?

Having Security:

Security is the protection an individual uses to insulate themselves from deliberate and intended threats. When Water types are preparing to leap into circumstances that have a lot of uncertainty, they need to consider what level of security they require to trust the journey. Definitions of security will vary, although usually they include a stockpiling of certain resources. For some, it's a ton of cash sitting in a bank account; for others, it's the basics of shelter, food, and community. There's no right or wrong answer, only what is true for you.

What does having security mean to you?

What does security look like?

What does it feel like in your body when you feel secure?

What's possible when security is present in your life?

Mediating Risks:

Every opportunity has risks. Some of these risks can be mediated, and others can't. When you can evaluate all of the working parts of a scenario, you are better able to go inward and listen to what your intuition is telling you, and then make the best decision for you. Water types find it helpful to rely on evidence from past experiences, as well as to assess their current level of safety and security, when working through the choices available to them regarding new opportunities.

How does using past experience assist you in mediating risks?

What information do you need to assess the risk of taking an opportunity?

What does it feel like in your body when you have mediated risks successfully and a situation has worked out?

What does it feel like in your body when you were unable to mediate risks and something didn't work out in your favor?

Did your intuition or bodily sensation help guide you in making decisions? If so, how?

Being Authentic:

The Water Element within us seeks authentic representation and requires the ability to transform based on changes in information and environment. For this reason, Water types can struggle to commit to long timelines and to meeting ambitious expectations. What if their viewpoint or direction changes? They want to ensure that if this happens, they can re-align to what feels authentic in that moment. To show up as themselves, Waters first have to understand what's important to them and trust their intuition. Their values and inner knowing will provide the information they need to express their truest selves.

What does being authentic mean to you?

What aspects of yourself need to be honored at all times?

What does it feel like in your body when you can be authentic?

What does it feel like in your body when you are compelled to hide your true self?

Feeling Free:

To be free is to be unrestrained in your actions and words, and to be able to authentically express yourself out in the world. Freedom has both external and internal aspects that must be navigated. You may not have much control over your external freedom due to life circumstances. But embodying freedom internally can have external consequences that may initially seem unimaginable. For Water types, it is important not to defer the need for freedom by thinking that x, y, and z have to align to experience it. Instead, they must commit to finding ways to experience freedom in the present, even when circumstances are difficult.

What is your personal definition of freedom?

What does freedom feel like in your body?

What small practices or decisions help you to embody and choose freedom?

What feels possible when you cultivate and choose freedom in your present circumstances?

Core Requirements of Wood

The Wood Element within each of us has the capacity to be assertive and powerful, and yearns to grow upward and strong so that we may stand tall, fully embodied in our truth. Wood types and those with a healthy amount of Wood in their Alchemy are driven to pursue forward momentum to expand and reach distant horizons. To keep the status quo is to perish.

When you engage in goal setting and execute your strategies, you can harness the core requirements of the Wood Element to help you stay the course, manifest your desires, and grow. Feeling empowered, implementing boundaries, following your truth, prioritizing growth and development, and having vision assist you in ascending to a realm of personal bests and reaching new levels of confidence.

Being Empowered:

New goals and dreams require you to feel empowered, perhaps even willing to risk standing out from the crowd. A Wood type knows that they can easily take themselves out of the running if they give other people's projections of their potential more importance than their own. Remember, you are the one who has to get energized to take action and believe that it's possible. Whether you turn to inspirational quotes, pep talks, or peers to cheerlead you onward, feeling empowered is what will carry you forward to the next steady step and beyond – to the finish line.

What does empowerment mean to you?

What do you require to feel or be empowered?

What strengths and skills do you possess that empower you to keep going?

Having Boundaries:

Boundaries provide supportive structure to allow you to stay true to your goals. They are the bumper rails keeping you focused on your priorities and ensuring that you continue along the path in the straightest line possible. For Wood types, boundaries act like green and red lights, telling them when to go and when to stop. This way they release unwanted guilt when deciding what to surrender and what to hold on to, thus ensuring that what's most important to them remains at the forefront of their awareness.

What does having boundaries mean to you?

What does enacting boundaries in support of your goal feel like?

What boundaries do you need to implement to support you right now?

Following Truth:

Truth is an embodied expression that often serves as a personal mantra or mission statement. For Wood types, knowing and being aligned with their truth helps give their actions and decisions integrity. However, first they have to develop an awareness of what their truth actually is. Without this, it can be easy to blur the lines and substitute another's convictions and truth as their own.

What does following your truth mean to you?

What does it feel like in your body to follow your truth?

What is your truth?

What is required of you to follow your truth?

What are words that you live by that embody your truth?

Growth and Development:

The Wood Element instills a sense of directionality that orients us to grow, seek self-improvement, and become better, stronger, more capable versions of ourselves. While navigating change can be difficult, staying the same makes us vulnerable to becoming weak, stuck and frail. Wood types are compelled to always look for opportunities to rise and evolve. This is where they thrive. In this way, they practice their skills and adapt to changing landscapes, so they are ready to take the steps necessary to reach their greatest potential.

What helps you to feel like you are growing, learning, and developing into the person you are meant to be?

What practices, tools, or studies assist in your evolution?

Currently, where are there opportunities for you to grow?

What are you reaching for right now?

Having Vision:

Without vision, it's incredibly difficult to cultivate the motivation to get started or to keep going in the face of adversity. Vision provides clarity on where you're going. Of course, the universe sometimes has other plans for you than the ones you make. However, usually a common thread weaves itself through both sets of plans, carrying the essence of your initial desire and the eventual outcome. Wood types need to be deeply connected to their vision to keep them engaged in a process from the dreaming phase to its execution; otherwise, they risk feeling lost in the weeds, unable to see a way through.

What do you currently see for yourself, your future, and your legacy?

What projects or action steps available to you right now align with your vision?

How does it feel in your body when you connect to your vision?

Core Requirements of Fire

The Fire Element within each of us longs to feel loved, seen, and heard. Those with a dominance of Fire in their Alchemy chart love deeply and fiercely, which can get them in trouble if they are reckless with their heart. It can also create a paradigm where they wish to be loved as they are but are afraid that others can't sustain the full intensity of their heat.

Naturally, the core requirements of the Fire Element pertain to matters of the heart. They focus on how individuals can create circumstances and relationships that are supportive of their full expression. They explore how you wish to give and receive love and affection, and to experience emotional stability, happiness, closeness, and commitment – all the ways you embody the innate truth that you are loved.

Giving and Receiving Love and Affection:

The Fire Element helps each of us open ourselves up to love and share our hearts with the people we love and the wider world. Fire types embody this openness by falling in love, bearing their heart, and giving affection as easily as they breathe air. All they want is to have that same love and affection reciprocated equally to reflect that they too are loved. While it's sometimes easier to experience this when you're in a loving relationship, it's just as important when you're not. Identifying how you wish to unconditionally love others – and yourself – will help you articulate your needs to a partner and establish practices of self-love to engage this requirement within yourself, for yourself.

How or what do you need in order to feel loved?

From others?

And more importantly from yourself?

What does it feel like when you give love and affection unconditionally?

What does it feel like when there are strings attached?

Feeling Emotionally Stable:

The Fire Element is passionate, frenetic, and intense. Fire types exhibit this behavior often by either burning hot – all in, consumed by their endeavor or fascination – or being out – turned off and really cold. The cycling from one to another can happen quite quickly or several times a day, which can feel unsettling. This is why it's so important for a Fire type to know which tools or practices of self-care help smooth the transitions and assist them to coming back to a stable center.

What does emotional stability feel like or look like to you?

What provides you emotional stability?

What practices support you coming back to a slow, sustainable burn?

Experiencing Happiness:

The energetic of Fire is light, warm, and upbeat, and Fire types are no different. Naturally bubbly and positive, they are the first ones to find the silver lining to any story. With a flash of their smile, they create warmth and happiness in almost every situation, inspiring others to be happy, too. The desire to experience happiness in their everyday life can leave a Fire type shouldering the responsibility to always bring the laughs and provide the entertainment. But this can push them into a performer role they may not always wish to embody. Being clear on how, when, and why they are participating allows Fire types to grant themselves permission to disengage and let others be responsible for their own happiness.

What does happiness feel like in your body?

What people, places and things bring you happiness?

How are you able to cultivate joy and happiness when you're alone?

When if ever do you feel responsible for others' happiness?

Feeling Closeness:

To feel connected to others is non-negotiable for human beings. In particular, we all require connection through physical touch, every day if possible. For a Fire type, being close to other people is necessary to thrive. Whether you are comfortable with public displays of affection or choose more private moments of intimacy, identifying the ways you require closeness and physicality in your relationships will allow you to better articulate how you prefer to connect with others.

How do you prefer to experience closeness with others?

How does the experience of closeness and physical touch feel in your body?

How often do you need to feel close to other people?

What activities or practices allow you to feel connected and in community with others?

Experiencing Commitment:

Given the hot and cold nature of the Fire Element, Fire types can find commitment elusive at times and often fraught with disappointment. Breaking down what commitment means to them can be a helpful exercise to get to the heart of what they really want, as opposed to what they've been socially conditioned to believe commitment is. This is an invitation to do some inner work to allow yourself to live in accordance with your personal definition of commitment.

What does the word commitment mean to you?

What does commitment look like?

What does it feel like?

What does it look or feel like when others are committing to you?

What does it look or feel like when you are committing to yourself?

Bringing the Core Requirements Full Circle

You may have come to the end of reading about each Element and their core requirements, and thought, "But I need all of these." That's certainly what I thought when I first engaged with this material.

You're not wrong. We do, in one way or another, need to embody all of these requirements to be whole. They support and build upon each other, especially when we apply them to different areas of our daily lives.

Answering the questions provided above will start the process of allowing the core requirements to support you as you need them to.

That said, it can feel overwhelming to reflect on all of these at one time. For this reason, I recommend that you start with your dominant and perhaps your secondary Elements. Through their lens, you can interpret others that carry less weight in your motivations and intentions. By keeping it simple and continually engaging with the requirements of your most dominant energetics, you will be able to easily reorient yourself back to your deep inner knowing and connect with your soul in an impactful way. Know that the other Elements will find harmony and turn up with their medicine when needed. Your soul is brilliant; trust it.

Part 2

Put Your Alchemy into Practice: Create a Life You Love

Chapter 8

Life's Governance & the 5 Elements

Now that you've established your personal Alchemy and learned how you are driven by your core requirements to seek comfort, control, and support, it's time to start putting this newfound understanding of WHO YOU ARE into practice. You and your Alchemy don't exist in a vacuum. Every day you interact with and come into relationship with different areas of your life, as well as other people. Knowing who you are is only half the equation. For it to mean something, you must now allow it to be the bridge from the life you currently have to the one you desire to live.

By now you may be aware that the 5 Elements are intricate, at times complicated. Their threads run deep into the fabric of our lives. Not only do they govern an entire medicine, the phases of nature, and our personality, they also govern major themes of everyday life. Taken all together, they create evidence that supports five innate truths:

You Are Enough,

You Are Worthy,

You are Safe,

You are Powerful,

You are Loved.

And these add up to the ultimate truth: You Are Whole. When you feel whole, you feel free to create a life fueled by love and legacy, where your impact ripples out beyond your knowing and intention.

In this section, we will explore the relationship of the Elements to areas of life.[24] To get started, I find that it's easiest to summarize these areas as themes, and then break them down into smaller details, so that we can connect with each of them on their own and together as a whole.

The Earth Element governs your Self-Love & Caretaking.

Naturally the Mother Earth energy weaves its way through how we care for ourselves and other people. As you delve deeper into this area in the next chapter, you will be guided to create greater harmony in your relationships and to make room for both self-care and care of others. In particular, we will emphasize practices that guide you back home to your body, through food, movement, rest, adornment, and pleasure, along with your caretaking responsibilities.

The Metal Element governs your Creativity & Credentials.

Within the energetics of Metal, you engage and embody your self-expression and purpose. Here, you consider how you project yourself out into the world, through your artistry, your education, and your awards and achievements. Whether you are splashing paint on a canvas, writing words on a page, or studying to get your master's or certificate, you are working to satisfy the core requirements of your inner Metal: having confidence and purpose in what you do, while being reverent to the inclinations of your soul.

The Water Element governs your Spirituality & Soul's Mandate.

Water with its depths and flow allows you to convene with the Divine and your intuition. Here, in the still, reflective space, you may open up to the organizing principles of your soul. As a result it becomes easier to

---

[24] Themes are inspired by Danielle Laporte's categorization of life areas in *The Desire Map* (2012, White Hot Press).

trust your intuition and align with your authentic nature. Through practices like ritual, prayer, and meditation, you create the opportunity to dream and to see, feel, and hear the bigger picture for your life and legacy. This isn't to say that you have to sit on a cushion saying OM. Water invites you to find your own way and be your own guru.

The Wood Element governs your Lifestyle & Livelihood.

The Wood Element empowers you to go for it, to make something happen. Just like the tiny sprout that bursts through the soil, the Wood Element governs the visible and somewhat material aspects of your life. Career, money, possessions, travel, and your capacity to set and achieve goals: all work together to support your innate drive to grow and evolve.

Lastly,

The Fire Element governs your Relationships & Service.

Fire types are all about love and connection, which is why it's no surprise that this Element governs all the different types of relationships we have with other people. From romance, to friendships, to family, the Fire Element creates the opportunity to erect supportive boundaries that allow intimacy to flourish. It also invites us to prioritize play and celebration, and to engage in collaboration, so that we may experience supportive communities and extend our love through philanthropy to make the world a better place.

Already, you may be inclined to start picking areas that you wish to improve. But before you rush ahead to the chapter calling your name, I invite you to first acknowledge each of these themes, Self-Love & Caretaking, Creativity & Credentials, Spirituality & Soul's Mandate, Lifestyle & Livelihood, and Relationships & Service, and notice which ones you're drawn to.

You may want to use the included chart and the writing prompts below to notice the overall ebb and flow of each category in your current life. This will provide you greater clarity on which Elements and areas are feeling supported and which you may wish to spend more time cultivating.

Much like the chart from the core requirements chapter, the goal is not to have each area fully satisfied all of the time; the purpose of this exercise is to give you a visual point of reference of the areas of focus and alignment that are occurring in your life at this time. If you would like to download a PDF version of this chart along with additional exercises to help you glean more insight, you can do that in the bonus section: www.ashleyabbs.com/5elementalchemy-resources.

Writing Prompts

How do I relate to each of these areas independently?

Are there certain areas that come into harmony and satisfaction more easily for me?

Are there areas I constantly struggle with?

Are there areas that I can't even begin to consider attending to because I'm so consumed with others?

The Pull of Your Dominant Element

Having spent some time considering the five areas of your life governed by the 5 Elements, you will notice some obvious differences in importance, as well as how each area is interpreted, based on your individual Alchemy.

Your dominant Element(s) is energetically going to pull you into the realms of life associated with that Element. This is in part because there is medicine within these areas to support your core requirements. For example, an Earth type can feel supported and nourished from food, rest, and movement. A Metal type can feel recognized and adequate through their education and accolades. Sometimes the areas of life associated with your dominant Element are where you flourish, but it's equally common that they represent your greatest struggles.

For example, many Earth types identify their greatest struggles as being food, movement, and taking care of themselves in the same way they care for others. Or Fire types that long for relationship and intimacy may have their hearts broken multiple times because they have so freely given themselves to partners who don't reciprocate the same feelings or level of vulnerability.

When we navigate the areas of our lives associated with our dominant Element, we may find it all-consuming. Other areas may appear to collapse, in part because there is no energy or attention being given to them. When this happens, the answer isn't to do more of what's not working. Instead, we can make a conscious effort to look to other areas to help lift us up. If study and creativity feel stifled, staring at your books or that blank canvas is likely not going to inspire new direction. But perhaps a spontaneous fun-filled day with your best friend might be just what you need to reignite your spark and create your greatest work to date.

Wood types can easily get pulled into putting everything they have into their work. Expecting the best of themselves, they push ahead to meet deadlines and chase the success they know is within their grasp if they just keep going. This can come at the expense of their relationships or eating at regular intervals. Ultimately, this tendency may lead them to being burned out and stressed, with cortisol levels through the roof. It may feel counterintuitive, but if they find themselves losing sight of their vision, a Wood type may experience healing through taking a day off, getting pampered, heading off into nature, unplugging, or moving their body. In slowing down for even just a couple of hours, they may be able to download the missing piece of the puzzle that brings their project together.

In the coming chapters, we will discuss each area in detail and provide writing prompts and tools to assist you in healing the areas of your life that you're finding particularly frustrating, but I would also like to invite you to look to areas that come to you with greater ease. By diverting some of your energy and attention to areas where you experience success and confidence, you may paradoxically find the fresh perspective and serenity you need to navigate the areas that cause you struggle and discomfort.

Writing Prompts

What is my current experience or relationship to the areas of life governed by my dominant Element?

Is there an apparent correlation between my dominant Element type and the areas of my life where I experience discomfort or struggle?

Are there areas not associated with my dominant Element where I experience ease? How might I call on these to support me?

What strengths of my Alchemy can I call on to support me in creating greater harmony in all areas of my life?

The Elemental Lens

You view the world through the lens of your Alchemy. So does everyone else. As my clients begin to really understand themselves and how they see the world, I encourage them to identify the dominant Element types of other people in their lives, including the teachers, authors, and speakers they follow. By doing so, they become aware of and can decipher the lens and motivations of these individuals, as well as where the information they are sharing is coming from. A Wood type will prioritize vision, work, lifestyle, and image; a Fire type, relationships, service, and being in community; a Water type, freedom, authenticity, and a connection to your Spirit/Source/God. When you understand others' motivations, you have greater context and can filter this information through your unique Alchemy lens. What part of their teaching or advice matters to you? Which aspects don't connect? In what ways can they support your Alchemy if it's different from theirs?

This is a critical step that is often missed in self-development. Quite often someone who's outside looking in at our lives can't comprehend why we're finding it so hard to get some momentum and move forward. They can see the way out of the hole we're in. They may have even clawed their way out of a similar hole. So, they wonder, why can't you?

Except their perception is built upon their lens and their Alchemy. If that area of life comes easily to them, then they won't necessarily identify with your struggle. It doesn't mean that they can't have compassion for you, but the tools and strategies they suggest to fix the situation or support you may not apply.

Of course, some of what they teach can still be helpful. It can be invaluable to enlist strategies, and borrow tools and supports from others to get you started. This allows you to try them on and see what works. At the same time, it's important to actively engage your own inner knowing, so that you may adapt or alter the strategies to support you more thoroughly. You do this by taking into account your Alchemy and unique core requirements.

For example, I'm an Earth dominant, Water secondary. I use soft, encouraging words and phrases such as "support," "nourish" and "authentic expression," to name a few, throughout this book. These words and the actions they entail reflect the lens through which I view the world. By using them, I hope to activate healing and self-expression in my clients and those I teach. But I recognize that those words likely don't land for everyone. While I've intended to mix it up and speak to each Element type in their own way, there are likely places in this text where you may wish to substitute your own words. Where I use the word "support," you may connect more to words like "empower," "initiate" or "catalyze," for example.

We look to teachers to help light the path and empower us to keep going. However, at some point, we must hold the torch ourselves and set forth in the direction of our destiny. The likelihood that you are going to achieve success exactly the same way someone else did is small. Even if you successfully reach your goal or achieve something important to you, in order to maintain long-lasting success or fulfillment, you will need to activate your Alchemy, requirements, and internal wisdom. Only by arriving at your own definition of success in each of these five areas of life can you live a life that you love on your own terms.

Writing Prompts

Am I able to identify the dominant Element of people closest to me?

How do their core requirements and the lens through which they see the world impact our relationship?

Of the people, personalities, coaches, writers, and mentors that I look to for direction, what is most likely their dominant Element?

Knowing this, am I able to discern how their lens is helpful to me? How it isn't?

The Ebb and Flow of Balance

The 5 Elements are always seeking balance. I know what you're about to say: "There's no such thing as balance," "Balance is a myth," "It's an impossible goal."

I hear you.

But let's drop the idea of balance as a scale with equal weights on each side. There are five Elements, not just two. Instead, I want to invite you to alter your perspective of what balance can be and see it as a reflection of your energy and priorities. The 5 Elements are present every waking moment of our existence, and they're in constant refinement, ebbing and flowing within each area of our lives to bring our attention and focus to what's most important in that time and space. When we seek balance with the Elements, we are looking to preserve our wholeness and uphold our priorities, not to place equal importance on all areas.

Your priorities are where your energy and intention go. When a priority takes up most of your time and focus, it will borrow resources that would normally be used to focus on something else. We all have moments and phases in our lives where we prioritize one specific area over another because that is what is required of us. This is especially true during transitions and big life events.

When a new baby comes into the home, it may seem like all you do is caretake and mother. You're too exhausted to think about work or worry about relationships with people not in your immediate circle. There is nothing wrong with this. Your focus and energy are exactly where they need to be. The Earth Element and its governance of self-care and caretaking will pull your attention from other Elements and areas deemed less important at this time. It will provide the medicine you need to feel supported while taking care of your beautiful baby, and remind you to be gentle with yourself and take exquisite care of your own body, mind, and soul's needs.

This same warping and pulling of energy can occur in any of the Elements. When we're in a new relationship and brimming with love and excitement, we're more willing to blow off our other responsibilities to spend just one more day cocooned in bed. Here, we are feeling the pull of Fire. When we're ready and eager to jump into a new project, we may devote all our time and energy into getting it off the ground, foregoing time with friends or self-care. This is the Wood energy pulling you into its realm.

When the energy relaxes and the phase cycles out – perhaps the project gets completed or your baby grows and needs less of your time – then you can return to holding a more global view of your life. At this point, you can widen your attention to include all the other areas of life and begin to cultivate energy that supports each part, so that the next time you encounter a big stressor, you may have greater supports to lean on. This may help it feel less all-consuming.

The idea that you will be able to divide your focus equally between the different areas of life, no matter the circumstances, is a farce. It's not going to happen, and vying for that form of perfection is damaging. However, you do have the opportunity to take a step back and notice where you spend your time and what you put the most emphasis on, whether it's due to social conditioning, identity, or ideals. This way you will know if your choices and direction are upholding the vision you have for yourself and will help you achieve your goals and desires.

If your choices and direction are aligned with your vision, you have achieved balance, even if some of the Elements in the last chart look to be underrepresented. Give yourself permission to allow your intentions and actions to remain as they are. You are living the life you're meant to live at this time. When things change and your priorities shift, you can reexamine where you're devoting your time and energy so that you can step wholeheartedly into the next evolution of you.

If you have not achieved balance, there's still an opportunity to course correct. By coming back to center and cultivating tools of support, you may be able to better uphold your priorities and find balance.

Writing Prompts

What area of my life am I currently consumed by?

What area or areas are currently not getting my attention?

Is the current balance supportive of the life I want to live?

Preparing for the Deep Dive

There is a lot of material packed into the upcoming chapters. To make the most of what you discover, remember your Alchemy and core requirements. I will be referencing them often. Keeping them top of mind will support you in connecting to your inner knowing so that the answers you seek come from within.

It's important to be incredibly compassionate with yourself as you spend time with the material and accompanying writing prompts. Take as much time as you need to work your way through each chapter. You may find you can move quite quickly through some parts, while others take time to digest and integrate in order to embody the medicine. When the latter happens, look to nature to guide you. Notice how that particular Element is influencing you in your environment. By doing this, you awaken a deeper form of listening to hear what your soul needs. You may even find yourself coming back to one area again and again. This is only natural. As you get closer to the incredible life that you are meant to have, a few pieces of the puzzle may prove harder to place. Keep following the voice within as it becomes more confident and sure of itself with each steady step you take toward your innate wholeness and a life that you love.

Your adventure awaits.

Chapter 9

Earth: Self-Love & Caretaking

I Am Enough

As we start our journey through the Elements as they relate and govern the different areas of our life, we begin again with the Earth Element. This is because the Earth Element helps us to affirm our current life experience so that we may fully embody new choices and the capacity for transformation. Before we can begin to create a life that we love, we must first fully acknowledge where we find ourselves in our present timeline. Unlike the energetics of the other four Elements, which invite either reflection or forward-thinking, the Earth Element centers us in the present, where we need to be to pivot between who we are right now and who we wish to be in the future.

Each of us will experience times when our inner Earth gets a little ungrounded. Often this occurs when we are missing important pieces of information or lack control of an outcome. In these moments, we may get too far ahead of ourselves and fixate on future timelines, which can lead to worry and rumination. But the Earth Element can help us course correct. All we need to do is stop whatever we are doing and come back to our bodies by first feeling into our feet and connecting to the ground beneath them. The reason this is so effective is because our bodies in Chinese medicine represent the pivot. The human form connects the heavens above and the earth below. Here, in between, through our lived experience we observe, perceive, and interact with the transitions of the seasons, flowing around and through us. The Earth Element orients us to start with ourselves, through the governance of self-love and caretaking. When we facilitate a greater relationship with this energetic, we become intimate with our soul and an active participant rather than an observer in our lives. In this way, through the Earth Element, we gain appreciation for the potency of the other Elements and the medicine they offer us.

The Earth Element invites us to acknowledge and integrate all the ways that we love, honor, and care for our body, mind, and emotions, as well as the ways we care and nurture other people. It asks us to be curious about the practices through which we love and care for our bodies, such as food, movement, and rest. It also encompasses how we experience pleasure and adorn ourselves to achieve greater coherence with our soul. And it spurs us to investigate our relationship to caretaking and "mothering" other people in our lives, such as children, spouses, friends, family or whomever you feel called to support.

Naturally, these areas are where we satisfy the core requirements of the Earth Element. Regardless of the amount of Earth you have in your personal Alchemy, healing and creating greater harmony in these areas will provide the opportunity to feel nourished, supported, and grounded, experience mental clarity, and be understood as the purest and truest expression of who you are.

Before you dive in, I want to point out that self-love is a verb. It's not something passive, and more importantly it doesn't have an agenda or goal. We know these things to be true of caretaking. We show up and do what is needed to support the people we love as they need support in that moment. We sit with them and hold space for the necessary conversations and feelings. The Earth Element extends an invitation to do the same for yourself: holding space and being present to your own needs to fully honor your soul. Self-love is in service of your body, your flesh, your mind, and your dreams. It has no agenda beyond asking, what do you need right now?

Do this now if you can. Close your eyes; place your hands on your heart and your belly, while pressing your feet firmly into the earth. Take a deep breath. Then, ask yourself the question: What do I need in this moment? Wait for your soul to answer in whatever form it chooses – words, images, sounds or a feeling. This is the next steady step or action that your soul is calling out for you to do.

Caretaking: Well-Rounded Nurturing

The Earth Element is often represented by the mother archetype. It's considered a stable energy that unconditionally loves, supports, and nourishes, welcoming others into its open arms. There is nothing that you need to do to experience this container of support. You are enough as you are. This energy is available to each of us to experience in all the ways we allow others to caretake us as well as how we authentically support and nurture individuals in our lives, whether they be family members, friends, clients, or colleagues.

Your circumstances and life experiences will affect how you engage with caretaking. When you're parenting, you may feel like you give everything you have, getting little in return. There may also be times in life when you find yourself relying on the tenderness or care of others, due to an illness or other circumstances where you require more support. What's important to remember is, like in every other area of your life, there is natural ebb and flow. Not every relationship is going to have equal give and take. And no relationship is static, therefore its caretaking dynamics might change over time. Also, caretaking can take many forms: emotional, physical, financial, and spiritual, to name a few. Being clear on, and willing to articulate, what you need and what you're compelled to offer will help make way for unconditional love and support to be both acknowledged and received.

Your Alchemy and core requirements will also provide direction and reveal your tendencies for how you wish to engage with this area of your life. Not everyone is meant to be a nursemaid or even a full-time stay-at-home parent. Those with a predominance of Earth generally feel well-suited to take on these types of roles. They have no trouble tapping into the great mother archetype. Where they tend to struggle is in articulating their own needs, if they haven't abandoned them completely, and in allowing others to care for them in their time of need. Other Element types are less likely to fall into this pattern; however, that doesn't mean they won't grapple in their own way with social conditioning about what it means to be a caretaker, parent, and even friend.

Receiving support and nurturing can feel awkward, or even embarrassing, as it requires allowing others to witness our vulnerabilities. As we age, we are taught to hide away the parts of ourselves that need support. Our culture values self-sufficiency and resiliency, and to admit we need help can be really difficult. I find that this is especially true for Metal and Wood types, as they both value these virtues and will choose to work things out on their own if possible. Fires, Waters and Earths may not always love the idea of letting someone in to help them out, but they will usually concede when it's apparent that it's in their best interest.

Acknowledging that caretaking isn't one-sided provides an opportunity to observe how it emerges within each of your relationships. Are you always the one making plans, organizing the get-togethers, and holding space for everyone and their feelings? If this is your reality, I invite you to become curious as to why that is. Are you willing to relinquish some of these tasks? Are your loved ones and friends capable of helping you? This may signal some deeper truths regarding your relationships (which we will discuss further in the Fire chapter). For now, just notice these tendencies and see how your awareness of them creates shifts. If you recognize that you seem to always be on the receiving end of someone's generosity, and you've been wondering how to become a better steward of your friendships, this is the perfect time to begin noticing where you can step up to provide a greater level of service toward the ones you love.

Writing Prompts

How do I want to nurture the different relationships in my life?

How do I want to be nurtured in the different relationships in my life?

What are some of the clues or feelings that arise that help me notice that I need to ask for support from others?

Who are the people I can lean on, who will hold space for me to be vulnerable?

Food: Nourish the Body, Fuel the Soul

Nourishment is one of the core requirements of the Earth Element. While food isn't the only way you can experience the feeling of being nourished, it is a cornerstone of how we reconcile this requirement. It also provides an opportunity to negotiate our perceptions of "enoughness," both in terms of being enough and having enough. When you are contented with yourself and trust that you will be provided for, then there's no need to hoard, gorge, restrict, or create a contentious relationship with the bounty that is provided to you. However, if you experience thoughts of lack or deprivation, it's instinctual to want to overcompensate by indulging and pushing past what you need to be satisfied. Even your cells, when they encounter restriction and deprivation, will store every morsel and calorie to prepare for the next time that you don't have enough.

In my practice I find that the individuals who struggle the most with food and the core requirement of nourishment are those with either an abundance of Earth or an extreme deficiency in Earth in their Alchemy chart. This is in part because the core requirement of being nourished requires reconciliation on so many levels. Your relationship to food is not something you can just put on the back burner. Food is a necessity of life; our bodies require that we engage with it in some way three to seven times every day. For those who struggle with it, this level of engagement can be overwhelming and further exacerbate the conflict. Which may lead them to want to abdicate autonomy over their food choices altogether and just follow someone else's rules. Unfortunately, it just doesn't work that way.

For food to be a foundational piece of your self-love – an initiation to what is nourishing and appropriate for you and your body – the answers have to come from within. Your body must lead the way. So, I'm not going to tell you what to eat. Sorry, (not sorry) if you were hoping for an Element type diet. I personally don't believe in them, and I don't instruct my patients on what or how to eat either based on their Element type. Yes, in Chinese medicine there are food energetics that can support the different organ systems to create greater harmony among the various excess or deficiency patterns. However, all of it, including the diet books in your local bookstore, must be taken lightly and filtered through the lens of your Alchemy (as well as the perspectives and motivations of the author or trainer's Alchemy too).

Instead, I'm going to invite you to slow down and become present with your body and your hunger, so that you can begin to ask yourself the right questions. What am I hungry for? What would be the most nourishing for my body right now? Sometimes the answer is going to be a beautiful piece of protein on a bed of wild rice and grilled veggies, and other times it's going to be chocolate cake. If control, deprivation, or dieting has been a part of your food journey, these questions have the potential to create a bit of a spiral. You may believe the only food your body wants is food that you consider to have little nutritional value, but I'm here to tell you that it's just not true. Trust your body and its wisdom. Two slices of pizza may feel really good, but six may not. Through trial and error, your body will tell you what feels right and nourishing and what doesn't. In time and with practice, the answers will come and lead to your highest good.

As you engage with food in perhaps a new way, I also want to be crystal clear that this isn't about eating just enough or restricting what you eat to the bare minimum requirements, under the guise that this is the proper definition of "enough." Not even close. If your body is starving, crying, or rumbling for more food, then clearly you have not given it enough nutrition. If this is the case, I would invite you to look at how this deprivation is rippling out into other areas of your self-care and life. Why and how are you denying yourself the ability to reconcile having and being enough in your life?

Writing Prompts

What is my current relationship to food and nourishment?

What am I hungry for?

What foods feel incredibly nourishing to my body right now?

What parallels can I see between my current relationship to food and nourishment and my belief that I am enough?

Movement: Move Some Qi However It Feels Good

Our bodies are meant to move. This is how we remain flexible, strong, and mobile throughout our lives. Movement encourages blood, and what we refer to as Qi in Chinese medicine, along with other fluids to be transported through the body, invigorating and regenerating our muscles to help combat the aging process. The way that our bodies are inclined to move may be different each day. For individuals who menstruate, your movement requirements and endurance will shift at different phases of your cycle. Where one phase may have you wanting to run or hit up a spin class, in another you may be called to slow down and perhaps spend time in a yoga nidra session or walk around your neighborhood.

Honoring the movement your body is asking for is an opportunity to develop and refine your skills of inner listening. Your body speaks to you about many things beyond whether it wants to run vs. dance. Listening to its cues and what it needs will assist you in creating a deeper connection to your intuition and inner knowing, while also helping you discern the symptoms that arise when your body requires greater attention and support. For empathic individuals, movement is also an incredible tool to dispel energy that you've picked up throughout the day that belongs to other people and isn't yours to hold on to.

I would also like to challenge the stereotype that movement as a form of self-love needs to be light and gentle. If your body is calling for the type of movement that leaves you laying in a puddle of your own sweat, do that! It can be incredibly healing and empowering to connect with the part of yourself that wants to reach for more.

Each of us will have tendencies for the type of movements that feel accessible and comfortable. Earths may gravitate to more yin-type, slow and steady forms of movement. Metals, a mix of running, cycling and yoga. Waters do best honoring their flow; anything in the water is going to soothe their soul at a deeper level. Woods tend to engage in yang-type activities, such as spin, running, HITT, etc., where they're pushing themselves and leaving it all on the floor. Lastly, Fires need movement to be fun, such as dancing. Anything that keeps it interesting is going to bring them inspiration and leave their heart singing for more.

That said, it can be transformational to engage in activities outside of our comfort zone. We especially benefit from participating in the realm of the other energetic (yin or yang) than we're used to. This can help us better listen to what our body really needs vs. what is routine and known. Take a class or two and discover what you like to do. It's okay to be a beginner, to fumble around at the back of the class or take stretch breaks if it becomes too difficult. We learn about ourselves when we try something new.

Writing Prompts

How does my body want to move and express itself?

What types of movement do I enjoy?

How can I curate time to move my body the way that it's asking to be moved each day?

What About Training?

Food and movement are two areas that also can be manipulated as tools in the pursuit of a goal. When this is the intention, you are straying from these two areas being simply foundations of your self-love repertoire. Instead, you're engaged in training. It's important to make that clarification. Training is how you move and fuel your body to achieve a goal, whether it's reaching a personal best, altering the overall physique of your body, finishing a marathon, or ending up at the top of a podium.

Training is amazing, and if most of your movement falls within these parameters, that is perfectly okay. However, I would like to suggest it's still possible to engage in movement that has nothing to do with your goals, because it serves a different purpose. You may be all about heavy lifting because you love how it feels and the way it shapes your muscles. Or you may be putting in miles in preparation for a big race. But you can still, once in a while, decide to hit up hot yoga because your body and soul require a change of pace and different form of movement. Or perhaps find yourself dancing in your kitchen after you drop the kids off from school, just because. That yoga session or 10-minute dance party not only doesn't detract from your training it can assist it.

When you bring awareness to your choices and actions, you will be better able to both plan for the goal and the type of movement and frequency you need to train, and also identify where there's freedom to go outside of your routine and move your body the way it desires to move. By letting your body lead, movement as a form of self-love can still be incorporated into your plan.

If you are not inclined to train for something, then don't. That doesn't mean you don't need to move. Our culture tends to valorize extremes of human behavior. We're either all in, because we're going for gold, or we're out, sitting on the couch or watching on the sidelines. Neither is sustainable, which is why it's important to experiment with different forms of movement so that you can find out what you truly love.

Writing Prompts

Is there something in particular I want to train for right now?

What is required of me to reach my goals, in regard to food and movement?

How can I still prioritize my self-love practices that relate to food and movement while I'm training?

Rest: Unplug to Recharge

Rest is so much more than sleep. While it's important to have a solid bedtime routine and good sleep hygiene, you also need to develop routines regarding when and how you work, as well as recognize how often you need to turn off and recharge your batteries with activities that promote rest and relaxation.

We are constantly downloading information. Modern conveniences like phones and tech combined with work expectations that we are always available lead us to be constantly on and performing in some way. Our culture capitalizes on this further by demanding that we continue striving and doing whatever is required until our work is done. The elusive carrot of rest and relaxation lies in wait as a reward.

Except there's always more work to be done. That needed break keeps getting pushed further out into the future. We touched on this topic in the Wood type chapter. This pattern of tunnel vision and charging ahead until a goal is completed, while putting off everything else, is one that most Wood types must constantly navigate or else their relationship to self-love and care is easily abandoned. Even if you don't identify as a Wood type, you too are probably very familiar with this narrative because our culture is Wood dominant. It holds those three weeks of vacation over everyone's head like a prize for falling in line and pressing ahead no matter the cost. Ignoring what you individually require in the form of rest and relaxation to be able to thrive.

Let's also not forget about housework, dishes, laundry, cleaning and whatever else you find yourself filling your time with. Many of us prioritize tasks over the rest that our bodies and minds require. This is problematic because there will always be more of these sorts of chores and activities to distract you from what you truly need. Use this as permission to just stop for a few minutes. Close the door to the laundry room. Have a basket that you can quickly throw the kids toys in so that you have a somewhat tidy room to drink your coffee and breathe without feeling guilty. You deserve time and space to put your feet up and let your mind unwind and experience peace. Breaking this conditioning can be uncomfortable. The tendency will be to fill the free time with something productive. Try not to do that. Trust me when I say that time away from your work, chores, and lists of to-do's is going to fuel your creativity and inspire new ideas and directions. And these in turn will have an even greater impact on your life, work, business, and family.

Tapping into how you wish to spend your downtime is going to provide you with options you can engage with on a day-to-day basis. These might include carving out moments that are uninterrupted by screens or distractions, reading a book, taking the dog for a long walk, or simply sitting with your morning tea or coffee and becoming present to the sensations of the heat and the silence, allowing your mind to quiet and possibly even dream. You may also start to consider bigger opportunities to immerse yourself in rest, such as going off-grid, attending retreats, being in supportive circles, or hiking in the wilderness. Perhaps you would prefer a luxurious hotel with room service, where you have time to hit up the spa and walk around the town with no agenda or timeline — which sounds absolutely divine. Your Alchemy and core requirements are also helpful guides in curating rituals, practices and getaways that allow your mind to make way to experience deeper reverence for yourself and perhaps act as a catalyst for you to discover the greater bounty of possibility available.

Writing Prompts

How often do I step away from my work and life responsibilities?

What boundaries do I require to support adequate time to devote to rest and relaxation?

What daily activities support me in experiencing rest and relaxation?

Are there retreats, trips or vacations that support my ability to rest and relax that require planning? Can I begin to research these and put one in my calendar?

Sacred No's and Soulful Yes's

In the Earth type chapter, we discussed why Earths can struggle to say no. The Earth Element reminds us that no matter what Element type you are, to make room for transformation and growth, you require mental bandwidth combined with a feeling of being in alignment with your priorities. Only then will there be the mental, physical and emotional space to devote your time and energy to bringing your soul's desires into form. This means that some of your roles, responsibilities and tasks have to take a back seat, so that you can catch your breath and zero in on what's most important to you.

When your mental bandwidth is taxed, you are quickly overwhelmed and unable to discern where you should put your efforts. Self-love practices are usually one of the first things to be pushed aside. In our culture, we are accustomed to spreading ourselves too thin, trying to be everything to everyone and always feeling like we are falling behind. In trying to do it all, we're basically playing whack-a-mole, rushing from one thing to the next, never fully present. This results in heightened levels of anxiety and numbing. When we're so oversaturated with tasks to get finished, it is easy to become increasingly frustrated with the fact that we aren't spending our time and energy on the parts of life we're feeling called to pay more attention to. Which is why it's so important for each of us to learn the word NO and use it as a sentence.

I like to encourage my clients who struggle with saying no to commit to the practice of sacred no's and soulful yes's. At the beginning of this exercise, they have to say five no's to opportunities and requests before they can say one yes. Naturally this can be quite difficult at first. You may find yourself turning down some really great opportunities; however, with each no, uttering the word without feeling compelled to offer an explanation becomes easier. Not only that, but clarity arises about what sort of opportunities and activities you wish to spend your precious time doing.

This practice can feel incredibly difficult for those who have learned to navigate their relationships by becoming people-pleasers and peacekeepers, especially those with a predominance of Earth in their chart. Other Element types may struggle less or find it only creeps in during particular instances in their life and work. If this is true for you, allow this to be confirmation that your time and your presence are valuable. Acknowledging your zone of genius and your priorities can assist you in realizing when you must delegate or ask for support. You can have it all, but you can't or don't have to do it all. Creating a life that you love requires that you have adequate time and space to devote yourself to the people and activities that will bring you closer to realizing those dreams. Where and how do you want to spend your time?

Writing Prompts

Where in my life do I feel overwhelmed?

With what or whom do I want to spend more of my time and energy?

When I think of saying no to someone or something, I feel…

What are five activities or requests that I can turn down, cancel or outsource to free up room for a soulful yes?

Pleasure: Borrowing a Spark of Fire

Engaging in pleasure for its own sake is the purest embodiment of an individual's belief in themselves. When I speak of pleasure in the context of the Earth Element and its fulfillments, I am talking about self-pleasure. There is of course intimacy and pleasure between partners; however, this sort of pleasure is governed by the Fire Element. Self-pleasure, on the other hand, is about enticing and activating the full capacity of our senses. Allowing yourself to be present to what your body, mind and spirit require to feel good and inspired.

If you're a Fire type, you might be exclaiming, "Finally!" This is your jam. Fires know that pleasure is a necessity, not a luxury. And they know all too well that the world can be a much more joyful place when you prioritize and experience pleasure on a regular basis.

If you're not a Fire type, then it's possible that the idea of experiencing pleasure may feel a little foreign, which is why I encourage you to take a cue from the Fire types in your life and borrow a little spark from their flame. This is helpful because Fire is considered the mother of the Earth Element in the generating cycle of Chinese medicine. It can provide a playful nudge toward experiencing a little more joy and not always taking life so seriously.

Our inner Earth connects us to the substance of our bodies, our muscles, our flesh, as well as to matter and the matrix of our planet. When we experience pleasure, we return to ourselves and revel in our own flesh. And in being with ourselves and finding delight in who that person is, we generate the capacity to feel free to take up even more space and experience life at its fullest.

Remember that you're in charge here. You control the experience and pace. Little practices, little steps, even baby ones, can be just as impactful as grand gestures and elaborate scenarios. Engaging your five senses of scent, touch, taste, sound, and sight will be key. Some examples to assist you to begin your own inquiry are hip circles, sensual movement, Qoya, masturbation, chocolate cacao ceremonies, jade egg practice, lighting candles and taking a long luxurious bath, taking yourself out on a date, having breakfast in bed, picking wildflowers, going skinny dipping, or going on an adventure. The only limiting factor is your own imagination or willingness to explore the landscape of what makes your soul come alive. For a list of resources check out www.ashleyabbs.com/5elementalchemy-resources.

Writing Prompts

What does pleasure feel like in my body?

How do I want to express my sensuality?

What activities or practices feel pleasurable to me?

What is one pleasurable practice or activity that I can do today?

Sacred Adornment: A Bridge to the Future You

Get quiet and still for a moment, and ask yourself, how does my body wish to be adorned? You may start to get a vision and sensation of a person that represents a future you. This person may be the embodiment of your truest and most authentic expression. Adornment is one of the most powerful ways to invoke the essence of your future self in the present.

As you sit with this image, you may find some visual cues that will help you begin making steps toward this you. You may not yet have all the pieces of the puzzle: what this future version of you does in the world or what their life looks like. At this moment, that doesn't matter. The other Elements in later chapters will help you to gain greater clarity on that. What's important here is allowing yourself permission to begin noticing how you might start to feel different and represent the person that you're becoming. What fabric is your body asking to be clothed in? What is your authentic style? How does the future you talk about themselves?

One of the most pivotal actions for me in reconciling my inner Earth and representing my purest essence was deciding to wear lipstick again. It sounds totally ridiculous when I write it out here, but for whatever reason, wearing a bright bold red lip brings me forward. It's as if I arrive through my lips and I am immediately brought into a higher form of presence. All it took was one simple action to show up more as my soul's authentic expression, which transforms my whole day and outlook.

Sacred adornment can be as simple as taking a few extra minutes to apply lotion to your skin or noticing your beauty in the mirror. Positive affirmations are another favorite of mine. Take a moment to tell yourself that you're beautiful and that you love your body. Adorning yourself with affirmations and compliments is a beautiful and powerful practice that each of us can apply daily with several repetitions.

The key to sacred adornment is that it's intentional. Whether it takes five minutes or hours, it doesn't matter as long as you're actively participating rather than just going through the motions so that you can get out the door. A very different energetic and medicine occurs when we adorn ourselves with purpose.

There are endless options for adornment: lipstick, sexy lingerie, makeup, scents and oils to anoint your skin, moisturizer, taking the time to do your hair, an evening gua sha routine, to name a few. The caveat to this invitation is a reminder that this area of our life isn't about upholding or replicating society's definitions of beauty. Instead, this practice supports being in right relationship with your most authentic expression. I invite you to notice what forms of adornment bring a sparkle to your eye and help to reframe how you show up in your life. Let the essence of your future self help guide you toward the most heartfelt embodiment of your essence. As you repeatedly engage with this practice, you will begin to discern the subtle difference in energies of what's impactful and what is not. A meditation to help guide you to connect to your future self's essence can be found in the bonus section at www.ashleyabbs.com/5elementalchemy-resources.

Writing Prompts

What is my current relationship with sacred adornment?

Taking cues from the essence of my future self, how does my body want to be adorned?

What verbal affirmations do my body and mind require?

What are one or two practices of sacred adornment that I would like to experiment with?

Filling Up Your Cup First

Our ability to love ourselves as much as we love and care for others is the purest embodiment of the Earth Element, confirming the innate truth that we are enough. Earth reminds us there's no need to label ourselves as selfish or selfless. We can remove the shackles of guilt for all the times when we felt we had to choose between ourselves and others.

Our culture glorifies the martyr, a person willing to abandon their own needs to care for others. This isn't really helpful when we are trying to feel good about ourselves and choose a life that we love. The Earth Element challenges our conditioning because it governs both self-love and caretaking. It is not one or the other; it's a microcosm of yin and yang. These are interdependent, and they can become imbalanced if one side takes up all our energy, thus depleting the other. Yet they can also be mutually supportive if we are willing to consciously engage each half. The more we take care of ourselves, the better we can take care of other people. Just as our willingness to care and hold space for others provides evidence that we are capable of doing the same for ourselves.

If you have a considerable amount of Earth in your chart, this whole chapter may have created some discord within your body and mind. This will be especially true if your general mode of operating is people-pleasing and caretaking to the point of exhaustion. There may be a really loud voice in your head coming up with objections to the ideas presented here. Telling you that you don't have time for self-care. Or maybe it's saying that too many people need you; you can't start saying no. You may have scoffed at some areas discussed in this chapter and dismissed them as vain or selfish. If that's the case, I invite you to take a breath and lean into this truth.

You cannot truly give to others what you don't give to yourself.

That's not to say you're not going to have feelings about it. Notice and acknowledge your judgments about doing one small thing for yourself and do it anyways. Look to your core requirements and see how you can further support them by small steady steps and actions. Try some of the suggestions outlined in this chapter or in the resources provided; experiment and see how you feel. Your body will give cues as to what it needs. Let it lead you. You are deserving of time, space, and devotion that is just for you.

Writing Prompts

I am enough just as I am, and I deserve…

Taking time to tend to my own needs supports…

A *Love Letter* to Your Inner Earth

You are enough just as you are. Nothing you can do will make this truer. You are loyal and loving, a safe refuge for every person in your awareness. There is nothing you wouldn't give to alleviate the suffering of another. Though I have to ask: Who's holding you while you hold everyone else? You do not need to carry the burdens of the world all on your own. There are capable hands that long to support and nourish you so that you may keep showing up for the people you love. It is safe to let others know what you need. They want to help. Let them.

At the center of your being, you're a peacekeeper. Creating harmony is as natural to you as breathing. But harmony that comes at the cost of yourself and your dreams is too high a price to pay. Your heart's desires are just as important as everyone else's. Though your stomach might churn and your voice tremble, I implore you to speak up and sing your soul's song. You've got this.

XO
Earth

Chapter 10

Metal: Creativity & Credentials

I Am Worthy

When we think about the Metal Element and its energetics, we are immediately presented with its duality. What we see on the outside are physical structures often characterized as hard, rigid, and ordered. Think of ore, metals, stones, gems, crystals, and mountains. But inside there is a hidden potential for transformation. Metals can be melded, melted, carved, and molded. Metal reminds us that properties can change and that transformation and greater gifts may be revealed if we're willing to look beyond the surface.

Stripping away the excess to reveal the purity of our true nature, and ultimately our inherent worthiness, is the gift that awaits us all when we engage and embody the Metal Element and its medicine. We start by acknowledging the outer wrapping of our identity and the roles that uphold and support our self-expression and influence how others perceive us. Then we press inward to recognize the inner aspects of our personality and identity that we choose to hide away from others and sometimes ourselves.

The Metal Element is the container in which the capacity for analytical, linear reductionism and unrestricted creativity exist side by side, as well as the bridge that allows for one to be sought within the other. This is why Metal so perfectly governs the areas of life related to creativity and credentials. It assists each of us in cultivating a deeper knowing of ourselves, turning our experiences and feelings into meaning and creative expression through our relationship to artistry, education, and awards or accolades.

Supported by Metal's core requirements – wanting to be recognized, experiencing a sense of completion, feeling and being adequate, and lastly, having purpose – we construct who we are and how we wish others to perceive us. This Element's realm is where each of us acquire the tools of our trade, gathering information and learning the rules, so that one day we may feel courageous enough to go out and add our own flavor and signature to the world. Here, we individuate ourselves from others, and our work from someone else's.

Metal can assist you in creating a purposeful life that makes you want to jump out of bed each morning, sure of your life path. However, there's a caveat. To access its full power, you must allow yourself to be un-done and enter the most vulnerable of places. To fully engage with the creative potential available to you, you must shed the armor of your perceptions, ideals, and beliefs about what is and what has to be. Because only when you surrender to the process of personal evolution can what's meant to be reveal itself.

Artistry: Curiosity and the Creativity of Your Soul

We are all artists in our own unique way. Some aspire to be artists in the conventional sense, by painting, writing, composing, etc. For others. we have to broaden our definition of artist to acknowledge that their form of artistry is deeply woven throughout their lived experience. Artistry is not relegated to arts and crafts; it can exist in the ways you orchestrate meetings, relationships, plans, events, proposals, etc. I consider an acupuncture treatment art in motion. It involves pulling together all the symptoms and diagnosing the patterns to form an intricate herbal decoction and point prescription that support a client's transformation or healing process. Your artistry is how you bestow your gifts out in the world for others to see.

Art is an extension of your soul freely expressed as form. When you make art, you make something out of nothing. The recipe is a combination of curiosity, skill, vulnerability, and a willingness to make mistakes and surrender to all possible outcomes. Your artistry is the catalyst to uncover new definitions, representations, and perceptions of beauty by allowing the heart to lead instead of the ego. To embody artistry requires a beginner's mindset and abandoning all allegiances to posturing and perfection. You do not have to have it all figured out. Instead, you prioritize process over product, and let the mishaps, epiphanies, and flashes of genius inspire a journey toward a destination that reveals itself in time.

Through the exercise of expressing your artistry out in the world, you create evidence that you and your unique contributions matter, both personally and to those who have had the privilege to witness your artistry in action. In this way, you tap into your soul's knowing and strengthen your relationship to your innate worthiness. Each time you step out to showcase your talents, you get closer to mastering your skill. No longer needing to follow someone else's lines or instruction, you can proudly display your gifts and begin to make your own rules, letting your heart and curiosity take over.

I believe it would be a disservice to all Element types to link certain Elements with particular forms of artistry. Instead, I think your core requirements will illuminate the intention behind your art and how it manifests into form. One factor that might determine your choice of artistry is how you want someone perceiving your art to feel and how it makes you feel. An Earth type may wish to exemplify support and nourishment; a Metal type, meaning and connection to enlightenment or purpose; a Water, introspection and freedom. A Wood may wish to engage with their vision and evolution of thought or direction; and a Fire, to inspire intimacy, connection, and love.

If you wish to bring more artistry into your life but don't know where to start, I invite you to first look at your hobbies. These may be ones you currently have, but if it's been some time since you've had the time or opportunity to engage with hobbies, think back to when you were young. In the prime of your creativity and imagination, how did you like to spend your time? Did you lose yourself in painting, drawing, singing, dancing, playing instruments, writing, building Lego sets and scenes to run your cars through? Did you enjoy wrecking what you created so that you could start over with the next idea? The freedom and flexibility you experienced then is still available to you now. Creativity will always be the solution to rigidity, and connecting to Metal's core requirement of discovering purpose is often a catalyst for being willing to put yourself out there in new and meaningful ways.

When I have clients who are struggling or feeling at a crossroads in their life especially as it relates to their jobs and identity, I will often redirect them to remembering who they were before they abandoned their artistry for activities that were deemed more productive or suitable because they pushed forward a certain agenda or met the expectations of others. What did they do before the rigidity of perfection narrowed their self-expression? Often the answers provide new directions, inspiration, and epiphanies. And these can lead to solutions that they would have never arrived at looking at a career catalog or course syllabus. Connecting these newfound directions to their Alchemy often provides additional confirmation to back their actions.

Writing Prompts

Where in my life do I currently express my art out in the world?

What activities or hobbies did I engage with in my youth?

In what ways are those qualities represented in my current form of art or artistry?

What activities of creative expression am I currently called to try?

Education: Learn, Practice, Execute

Anything that we aim to do adequately requires time, energy, and practice, practice, and more practice. It doesn't matter whether you're acquiring knowledge on the way to earning a certificate or degree, doing something physical like a sport where you're aiming to achieve your personal best, or just being a living, breathing human in the school of life. Learning and education are lifelong pursuits, and they're important ones. They allow us to engage with those things we're most curious about and incorporate them into our identity and perhaps our greater purpose.

Education is an opportunity to create new pathways that bridge the gap from where you are to where you want to go – a place where you fully embody your individual expression and activate your unique zone of genius. This is where you take something that started out as a whisper in your heart and you embark on a quest to know more, to achieve the level of execution and expertise that you desire.

Everyone's definition of education and choice of curriculum will look and be different. Some individuals will pursue education in the most obvious sense, in the form of degrees and higher education, to execute their purpose within the realms of academia and their profession. This is a common trajectory among Metal types. However, education is not limited to just school. For others, education will center around emotional, relationship or spiritual endeavors. Either way, your chosen curriculum acts as the catalyst for you to devour more information and bring greater levels of proficiency and adequacy into your life, thus further crystallizing your identity. In essence, you are proclaiming, "This is who I am, and this is what I know."

One very important thing to remember is that education doesn't count for much unless you put what you learn into practice. It's very easy to stay in the learning phase of your journey, acquiring information but never integrating it into your real-world experience. For example, you can very well choose to stay in school acquiring degrees, without ever taking a position or job where you can actually use your skills. I've seen many would-be entrepreneurs take a million business courses and never launch their business. The same can be said for some athletes who train their butts off every day but never actually compete.

Education is a beautiful container in which to explore ourselves and what we're capable of, but it's easy to fall into a pattern of consumption without transformation. For example, Waters love the knowing and sometimes aren't so invested in the doing, whereas Woods know that learning and growth occur when you leap forward and put what you know into action. The rest of the types tend to fall somewhere in the middle. Usually, when someone gets stuck in the realm of education, the motivator is fear. And it's an indication that certain core requirements related to adequacy aren't being met, causing you to believe that you don't know enough yet to move ahead. Let's acknowledge that there is a sense of safety when you're just learning. Sure, you may be judged on performance or receive grades, but the stakes are much lower than when you're tested in real-world situations.

At some point, if you never complete your education, the process of learning will stagnate. You will be unable to fully embody what your education can offer you. And until you start doing, you won't reach the next stage of learning. If you find yourself at this point, it's time to put yourself out there to spur your greater evolution. Only then will the next steps, the ones taking you where you are meant to go, be revealed.

When clients have struggled in this area, I have found it helpful to encourage them to take an honest look at their education (in whatever form) and list out their evidence of skill. Write out what you have learned – the theories, skills, traits. This might look like a CV or resume, or be a list of training or skills you can execute under pressure. Then calculate and log the number of hours and the amount of money you've spent. Look at it all in black and white. Take it in. Now let yourself recognize just how many amazing things you can do. Put them front and center to remind you of what you're capable of, so that you can then go out and do them.

Writing Prompts

Make a list of your education, skills, training, hours, etc.

What three skills can I choose to highlight and execute today in my life or work?

What am I feeling called to learn next?

Awards and Achievements:
Internal and External Motivators for Validation

The Metal Element longs to be recognized. This is one of its core requirements. The Metal within you wishes to be seen and appreciated. It wants acknowledgment and credit for your efforts by peers, family members and the larger community. This recognition may come in various forms: words, actions, certificates, maybe even an evening thrown in your honor. Or sometimes it literally takes metallic form: as a trophy or medal. No wonder metals can be shiny, gleaming and beautiful. They aspire to be noticed!

Depending on your Alchemy and core requirements, your preference for validation will differ. If you're a Fire, anything with a stage and spotlight is going to be up your alley. Maybe that well-rehearsed Oscar speech will come in handy as you express your thanks and appreciation. For those less inclined to be front and center, having a diploma hung on the wall behind your desk, or kind words and/or a promotion from your boss may be more than acceptable recognition and appreciation for your experience and efforts.

Regardless of your preference, awards, achievements, and credentials can provide both external and internal motivation.

Pursuing and receiving awards can confirm that your time, money, effort, etc., were worth it. They show that you had the purpose, work ethic, and ability to bring something to completion, all traits a Metal Element adores. Often due to this acquired hardware or credential, a grander path begins to emerge, and an identity further crystallizes. Awards and accolades are not just window dressing. They can help you catapult your career or purpose far beyond what you might have thought possible. This aspect of receiving awards and being recognized for our accomplishments is exciting and worth celebrating.

Where we must be wary of putting too much emphasis on awards and other outer manifestations of achievement is collecting them without acknowledging why we're pursuing them. To blindly reach for the next trophy or level of achievement without fully integrating past accomplishments is to merely collect knickknacks that clutter your walls or end up in a shoebox. Or worse, it could tie you to a trajectory or destiny that no longer lights you up. With every completed goal and award, there is an opportunity to look inward to our intrinsic motivations to affirm our intention and purpose. In this way, we ensure that our next goal or achievement is aligned with our soul's truest expression and exemplifies the person we are becoming.

Ask yourself not only why you want an accolade but also how it will be connected to your greater purpose. Being fully transparent with your motivations will allow you to recognize when the path you're on has come to its natural end. Or, inversely, it can confirm your path, and thereby help you overcome setbacks or obstacles. In this way, you set the stage to fully embrace your inherent worthiness and let your abilities shine through as you reach for your intended goal.

Whether it's a four-year degree, a competitive season, or a 30-day challenge, starting and seeing something through to completion can inspire new levels and layers of self-exploration. You will learn something about your potential, your perseverance, and the areas where greater growth and evolution lie. An award in whatever form, even one that you create for yourself, can provide the incentive to keep going, even when you don't think you can take another step, and emphasizes the importance of your intrinsic motivation over relying on external validation to confirm your worthiness.

Writing Prompts

What awards or credentials have I achieved?

Which awards or achievements have helped to define or create my identity?

Which awards or achievements have I outgrown? Why?

What is an award or achievement that I currently have my sights set on?

Perfectionism: Protection, Control and Personal Excellence

The Metal Element is sharp, refined, and precise. These are also qualities each of us can cultivate when we engage with this Element to better facilitate our artistry, skill, expertise, and self-expression. There's a fine line, however, between pursuing personal excellence and pursuing perfectionism. The latter threatens to create disharmony in the Metal Element, by cutting us off from our heart and inner knowing. It can lead us to become overly critical, rigid and controlling of what is acceptable when expressing one's gifts out in the wider world.

Our motive in pursuing perfection and trying to make everything look bright and shiny is that we want to control the outcome. Perhaps this outcome includes achieving recognition or an award, or perhaps we simply wish to circumvent any judgment or criticism. Perfection is appealing because it can be worn like armor. It makes our insecurities invulnerable to exposure. However, that armor comes at a cost. It means quieting or ignoring the inclinations of our souls calling us to try something new, even if that requires taking on the role of the beginner and opening ourselves up to making mistakes. It can also create greater rigidity in our perceptions of what success and completion look like. This can cut off creativity and new opportunities that could hold the capacity for outcomes more fulfilling, impactful, and grand than what we can currently imagine.

Perfectionism creeps into the psyche through use of comparison, procrastination, and negative self-talk (often referred to in modern psychology as your inner critic). Comparison uses other people and their highlight reel as a barometer for belonging. Your inner Metal, with its soft, gooey center underneath that tough exterior, just wants to be accepted, recognized, and appreciated for its efforts, and can easily get stuck thinking that everyone else is more qualified or has done something better than you. Why bother? your inner Metal might ask. Perfection through procrastination often takes the form of a moving end goal. If you believe more skills, proficiencies or accolades are required before you can move ahead, you may never get to the next phase or level.

Both these manifestations of perfectionism can be intensified by your inner critic. This little voice can cite every time you've received criticism, experienced a correction or judgment, or were shamed or bullied. These incidents have been internalized, crystallizing certain beliefs and insecurities. Your inner critic then recalls them every time you question your worthiness and capabilities. Even with all the inner work you've already done in this chapter – acknowledging your creativity, skill and achievements – your inner critic can still bore tiny holes in your confidence to sow the seeds of doubt and prevent you from creating a life that you love. It's a saboteur of your efforts, halting your progress even when your soul is backing you every step of the way. However, it's important to note that your inner critic isn't necessarily acting out of malice. Instead, it's working very hard, in an intricate and clever way, to keep you safe and insulate you from getting hurt or being disappointed while trying to reach greater heights.

In fact, aspiring for perfection isn't all bad. Being intrinsically motivated to improve yourself is necessary to spur growth and evolvement. This is how you learn your craft and perform with a high level of expertise and execution. Athletes are motivated by perfection to achieve personal excellence, practicing their skills over and over again. This way, when they get in front of a crowd and must negotiate additional adrenaline and nerves, they have a better chance to perform those skills with the same ease. Surgeons practice their techniques repeatedly because another person's life depends on them. You probably have spent immense amounts of time studying, training, and practicing something to achieve a degree of expertise and confidence that you know what you're doing. This is why it's so important to acknowledge where the pursuit of perfection is assisting you to go further inward and affirm conviction in your soul's expression, or where it's inhibiting you from leading your extraordinary life.

How do you know when perfectionism is inhibiting your soul's self-expression?

- You're stuck in comparison, thinking that everyone else is doing better than you.

- You're procrastinating, always moving the target of when you'll be ready.
- You're doubting yourself, asking questions such as "Who am I to..." or "Why me?"
- Your beliefs about your worthiness are tied to an outcome you have no control over.
- You are attached to a specific outcome and unable to entertain other opportunities that appear different from what you've deemed acceptable.

Writing Prompts

How does perfection show up in my life to inhibit my self-expression?

In what areas of my life do I currently compare myself to others?

How do these comparisons inhibit my self-expression?

Where in my life am I procrastinating and why?

What does procrastination look like?

What words or phrases does my inner critic use to prevent me from moving forward?

In what ways is the pursuit of perfection inspiring me to reach personal excellence?

Navigating the Loss of Identity: Re-Qualifying Worthiness

Identity can be a fragile construct. We spend a lot of time, energy and money striving to create it, believing that our outer appearance – how we move through the world and the way others perceive us – is what matters most. We buy in and believe that our worthiness is tied to titles, recognition and validation. Ideally this outward manifestation of our personality and roles reflects our soul's expression, but that isn't always the case – in part because our identity isn't as fixed as we perceive it to be and in part because it is actually meant to be constructed from the inside out, not the other way around. When we allow our soul to lead, our identity can shift, change, and evolve as we grow and experience more of what life has to offer us. But if we hinge our worthiness on external factors, like labels and appearances, we can get stuck operating in a closed circuit, tied to a fixed identity that can't change with circumstances or our soul's transformation.

This can particularly become an issue when we experience a loss of identity. Whether this occurs because we outgrew our old self or because it was stripped away due to circumstances, the result can be disorienting and leave us feeling lost.

When a key way you describe yourself changes or ends, you're inevitably confronted with the question: Who am I? Perhaps you've lost your job, or your marriage has ended. You retired. Maybe you got sick, or possibly it's the fact that you got better. In some of these scenarios, these shifts may be accompanied by a sense of freedom. If you've just retired, you can finally do all the things that you've put off. In fact, you can do anything you want. But in time, after the honeymoon phase, without distractions or numbing, melancholy can set in. You may feel haunted by the person you thought you were but aren't anymore. This will require the appropriate reconciliation, including perhaps navigating a stage of grief and saying goodbye to your former self to achieve closure.

Depending on your lived experience, you may undergo this process many times over. Sometimes the shifts in identity will be very apparent and expected. Others are so subtle you may not initially recognize them as a loss, such as the transition from being a young adult with little responsibility to becoming a husband or wife, or a parent with a job. While our culture considers this a natural stage of growing up, that doesn't mean that a loss of identity hasn't occurred. Letting go of who you were when you were single and free might need to be recognized. Navigating these losses, big and small, in whatever form they come, requires tenderness and the utmost compassion for yourself as you unhook all the ways you have tied your worthiness to identities that are no longer yours.

This may require you to grieve, cry, and feel momentarily bereft of purpose. You may wish to rush through this process of shedding skins of the past to make way for the future. It's likely going to feel uncomfortable. However, if you're able to remain present to your feelings and thoughts, the potential for alchemy is available. To turn lead into gold, so to speak, you can redefine your worthiness so it's not about what you do or how you present yourself, but about who you are. Bringing closure to a chapter of your life doesn't need to be an ending; it can be a beginning. It can mentor you and be evidence of your resiliency and abilities. All you have to do is allow your soul's expression to lead, fully believing that you're worthy even if you don't yet know where you're going or what you want to do. This is an opportunity to fully surrender to the waves of possibility that will come forth if you are open to them.

If you're unsure how to fill your time, reflect on your Alchemy's core requirements, and start with art in a form that feels aligned. Pick up a hobby, seek joy, be curious, and remain aware to when those sparks of inspiration begin to shift to a yearning for something greater. You will know when you require more information and knowledge, when play needs to transform into practice. You will not need to force it; it will just flow.

Writing Prompts

What identities have I lost or surrendered from my past?

How do these identities still dictate or inform my decisions?

What identities am I being asked to surrender at this time?

What have I learned from my former identities?

How can these lessons from my past mentor me moving forward?

Gratitude: A Bridge to Reverence

In Chinese medicine, the Metal Element governs the lungs and breath. With it comes the invitation to create greater reverence and appreciation for the preciousness of life itself. A single breath, from inhale through to exhale, brings you to the space between what was, what is, and what will be. We breathe without thinking about it most of the time; frankly, it's nothing short of extraordinary. But there's also incredible power in breathing deliberately. Within just a few breaths, you can recalibrate the body, removing the "fight or flight" response of the sympathetic nervous system (SNS) and replacing it with the more relaxed and generative response of the parasympathetic nervous system (PNS).[25] In this way, you reduce stress and anxiety, and help fuel your creativity and attention, so you can find resonance in the things you choose to do. Lighting your path and illuminating your life's purpose.

The key to accessing this transformative ability of the breath is gratitude. Gratitude helps pull the mind into the present, so that it may become aware of the body – reinforcing Metal with the Earth Element – and your breath. When you allow the here and now to reign, you naturally focus on what's most important, rather than where the future may take you. You can try this now. Breathe in for one, two, three, four, hold, and then exhale out one, two, three, four, five. Repeat this interval for five to seven cycles. As you breathe, bring into your awareness people, places, and experiences that you are grateful for. Practice this and you will soon see your ability to discern what is important and what isn't become stronger.

Gratitude, as a practice, applies checks and balances to your ambition so that you remain deeply rooted in integrity with your soul and aligned with your purpose. With a grateful heart, you can stay connected and true to your North Star while also ensuring that the people and things you hold dear remain top of mind as you design the life of your dreams. You may also want to acknowledge lessons and gifts from past experiences, to provide closure and decide which of these should come with you into your next chapter.

---

[25] Brown, R. P., & Gerbarg, P. L. (2009). Yoga breathing, meditation, and longevity. *Ann N Y Acad Sci. 1172*, 54–62.

Gratitude has this unique ability to refine, reorganize and remove obstacles that appear to be fixed or permanent. It's as if time and space bend to support your deepest needs and desires, and renew your perspective on what's possible. It transports you out of loops of comparison. It undoes the lure of perfectionism and silences the inner critic that works so hard to make you doubt your abilities. It brings you back to trust and affirms that all that is good is working in your favor. Thus, it imparts a vibration of worthiness and joy into the rhythm of your consciousness to set your potential legacy in motion. Suddenly, you will be able to recognize what's working, what tools and skills are actually required, as well as what no longer needs to take up space in your bandwidth.

It almost seems too simple to be true – that a gratitude practice combined with your breath can teleport you to new opportunities – except that it is and it does. A few moments at either the start or end of your day will usher in new light and possibility. All it takes is developing reverence for the way your body breathes while listening to your heart whisper the love and goodness that is available to you in this moment.

Writing Prompts

What in my life am I currently grateful for?

Who in my life am I currently grateful for?

How are the people and things that I hold most dear a part of my future dreams and desires?

A *Love Letter* to Your Inner Metal

You're hard working, precious, and objective, with an eye for detail that makes you skilled at whatever you put your mind to. You expect the very best of yourself, inspiring others to rise along with you to new heights and personal bests. Don't let your need for everything to be perfect prevent you from noticing all the good that has occurred as a result of the life you've already lived.

Remember to take a step back and recognize how your life reflects your expertise, your ethics, and your artistry. It's all right here. Let go of the places where you feel you need to struggle, and instead breathe this in: You are worthy. You are deserving of every single good thing that has come your way. Enjoy yourself. The best is still to come.

XO
Metal

Chapter 11

Water: Spirituality & Soul's Mandate

I Am Safe

The deepest part of who you are can be accessed with the Water Element. Here, we drop in and listen to the vibration of our being, seek answers and realize our greatest potential. We see how the depths of our soul are closely intertwined with the Divine. The Water Element is where our past, present, and future timelines all coalesce to inform our intuition, reveal our next steady step, and inspire us to leap into the unknown.

First, you must strip away the distractions and excesses to experience the raw you. Only then can you realize what you actually need to move forward. The Water Element guides us, physiologically, mentally, emotionally, and spiritually, in consolidating our resources and then using them to seek authentic expression and make ripples of impact beyond our knowing. It is responsible for the overall feeling of protection and safety – and the courage we have when we know ourselves at our core – that give us leave to be free and trust our inner wisdom, so that we may leap toward the callings of our soul.

The Water Element is considered the densest energetic of all five Elements and always illustrated as occupying the lowest space on an Element chart. Even a water droplet, its tiniest form, will always flow downward and pool with all the other droplets at the lowest point available and settle into stillness. That is, until a force directs it or a catalyst transforms it, causing it to follow the flow. Considered the most yin of the Elements, Water also has the beginnings of yang available to it. While its associations with stillness, receptivity, and reflection get much attention, the yang force, in the form of inspired action, can rise up and reveal itself in serendipitous moments and steady steps that we can trust.

The areas in which we engage with the potentiality of Water are all related to the soul and its connection to the Divine. They are conduits through which we can access our inner wisdom, quiet our minds, and get comfortable being uncomfortable with a blank slate. Practices connected to rituals, dreaming, prayer, meditation, and learning to trust our intuition over someone else's each hold space for us to harness our untapped potential and create a reality that looks entirely different from old plans and expectations. Instead, we get the opportunity to rewrite our destiny and be our own guru.

Rituals – Structures that Support Your Freedom

The Water Element can bring with it a lot of feelings, and usually more questions than answers in the beginning. This is natural. When we're on the verge of new opportunities or directions because older models no longer fit or serve us, it's easy to become overwhelmed or anxious. Rituals can serve as a container, borrowing the structure and organization of the Metal Element, to hold the potency of the Water energetic. They provide firm entry and exit points to prevent us from feeling lost or becoming overwhelmed by emotions we may not be fully ready to feel. At the same time, they allow us to connect to our soul and the initiation to experience something bigger than ourselves.

Ritual provides a sacred space to convene with what you might call the Divine, God, Spirit, Tao, Love, or the Universe. You may have your own word for the unseen energetic that weaves the threads of our destiny together. It is through our relationship with this force that we seek understanding of ourselves and hopefully arrive at the next steady step that propels us toward our destiny.

You may already have established rituals because they have been passed down to you or come from your practices of faith. Or this may be entirely new to you. If the latter is the case, I invite you to start with something simple. Choose one intentional action to get to know the energetic and medicine of this Element. It's common in my practice for clients to have trouble even entertaining the thought of participating in a ritual. Often this recoil is caused by previous experiences in church or as a child experiencing family traditions that didn't feel supportive or safe. If this is you, then I invite you to first explore what ritual has meant to you. You may also want to journal about any old stories from your past that might be preventing you from doing this exercise. Once you've done that, you can start to reframe what ritual means and welcome it into your life in a new way.

Some Element types prefer rituals over others. It's my experience that Metals and Waters have an affinity for them, especially the more traditional ones we are familiar with. Time allocated to convene with ceremony and stillness assists Metals in their seeking of higher meaning and connection. For Waters, this can be a way to weather the ever-changing ocean of emotion and their souls' calling for greater authenticity and depth. This is not to say that the other three types don't engage with rituals. However, I've often found they experience barriers due to pre-defined conceptions of what rituals are and should look like that don't serve their type's essence and natural tendencies. For Earths, engaging with ritual can feel like one more thing on their to-do list. Rituals imply an extended commitment, which can be daunting to Earths who are already overextended in terms of time and energy. Committing to rituals can feel like a setup for breaking yet another promise to themselves. Wood types sometimes see rituals as a waste of time. "Why talk and think about it when you can just do it?" is the Wood's mentality. On closer look, however, they often have rituals; they just don't define them as such. Instead, they might consider them routines or preparations. These are the little things they do that invite them to slow down or unwind, like a workout or a glass of wine. Fires, on the other hand, love ritual, but they don't necessarily want to do the same thing every single day because that can be boring and unfulfilling. Joy or the seeking of joy leads all their actions. It can be trial and error until they find the perfect combination of actions that provides that deeper connection to their soul through their heart's joy.

There's freedom to be curious and experiment with creating your own rituals. Now before you go and buy every oracle card and crystal at your New Age bookshop, I want to remind you that ritual can really be anything you feel called to create. Your imagination is really your only limiting factor. All you need is you, your intention, and the time and space to connect to the Divine. Often there are moments in our daily schedules that could be ritualized with only a bit of reorganization and intention. For example, rather than guzzling down your morning cup of coffee on your way out the door, take a few extra moments to sit and be with your thoughts. Your morning yoga practice can be more than exercise; you can connect to it as it was originally conceived, as prayer through movement. I find my self-care practices can also serve as a ritual to help me engage this area of my life, while also clarifying my energy so that I'm not merely going through the motions.

These actions and so many more can affirm that you are showing up for all parts of yourself, not just the parts necessary to complete your to-do lists and goals. Without ritual, it's easy to bypass the spiritual areas of life altogether. In this realm, there are more questions than answers, which can feel frustrating and at times defeating. No one wants to feel lost or uncertain about what the future holds. To avoid this, many of us choose to live in a state of reactivity. But if we continue to do this without engaging with the larger questions, we will find ourselves right back where we started, or possibly more in the dark than we were before. Take your time figuring out what your specific rituals are. Trust where you feel more reverent and more present to your inner landscape of thoughts and emotions, as these will reveal which actions and intentions feel the most authentic for you.

Writing Prompts

What is my personal definition of ritual?

What actions, intentions or ritualized activities help me foster sacred space to engage with my soul?

Dreaming: Tapping into the Bigger Picture

Dreaming is a Watery phenomenon that mostly occurs when we are at rest, particularly in the deepest point of sleep known as REM.[26] We don't have much control over this dreaming as it often transports us to realms that lack all boundaries, including the rules of space and time.

When we're upright and waking, dreaming takes a different form. Daydreaming is more active, and obviously it requires our participation. You may have been told as a child to stop daydreaming and get your head out of the clouds, but it's actually important that we regularly and intentionally create time to imagine ourselves in alternative places and timelines. Using our imaginations to stretch beyond the edges of our reality, we can glimpse wisdom and prophecy connecting us to our greater destiny.

Perhaps it's my Watery nature, but I can't imagine going a single day without opening myself up to the threads of destiny that are still beyond my grasp. I recognize, however, that this may be easier for some types than others. Woods, who require vision, harness their active imaginations to help propel their goals and ambition. Fires allow dreaming to fuel their desire for greater connection and happiness. Earths and Metals, who tend to err more on the side of practicality and the concrete, sometimes view daydreaming as a waste of time and choose to confine their engagement to their current reality.

If you have rituals dedicated to spending time with your dreams and alternate realities, then I want to confirm how worthwhile and important these are to your growth and evolution. But if you're not sure where to start, I would like to suggest some prompts that I use myself and with my clients to help explore our greater dreams and desires.

---

[26] Brain basics: Understanding sleep. (2019). https://www.ninds.nih.gov/ Disorders/Patient-Caregiver-Education/Understanding-Sleep

First off, remember this is an opportunity to reach for the stars. In the beginning stages of active dreaming, you can ignore your pragmatic and rational mind, and remove the filters of what's practical or possible in your current life. It's especially important to not confine yourself to what you think you deserve. It's so much easier to bring a dream back to earth than it is to try to make it bigger after the fact.

I encourage you to get out your journal and right now, while you're already engaged with this energetic, begin to write out your dreams. Start with your ideal day, ideal job, ideal body, ideal relationship, ideal income, etc. Write whatever comes to mind when you ask yourself, "What do I want?"

Allow yourself to get really clear and specific about this, and please don't hold back. Let your heart and soul speak up. You do not need to apologize to anyone for what comes out. You may be surprised by what you write. You may be able to do this in one sitting or it may come through in waves each time you perform your rituals and get little glimpses from your heart. If the latter is the case, have a small notebook or a dedicated place on your phone where you can jot down these whispers. You may also find it helpful to notice your dreams at night, try to be more aware of what's happening around you, seek inspiration, or journal often. And always remember the power of intentional breathing.

I would also like to remind you that at this stage you do not need to get caught up with the logistics and "how's" of making your dreams a reality. At this moment, you're capturing the essence of your soul; the steady steps and form will come in their own time. What's most important is that you begin. When you create reverence for your dreams and the nudges of your soul, your destiny will appear.

Writing Prompts

What do I want?

What does my ideal job look and feel like?

What does my ideal body look and feel like?

What does my ideal relationship look and feel like?

What does my free time look and feel like?

What does my spiritual practice look and feel like?

What does my ideal abundance look and feel like?

What does my ideal day look like from beginning to end?

Prayer: I'm Willing to Do My Part

Often when we catch a glimpse of a future timeline, we feel like we're stuck in a space in between. We know where we want to go, but we don't yet have the tools or specifics on how we're going to make it happen. Sometimes, there is nothing we can do at that moment; the next steps are in the hands of other people or the Divine. This can be frustrating. Regardless of your best efforts, you can't will the future you dream of to come any quicker. All that is left to do is loosen your grip, surrender your expectations, and pray for the guidance, patience and inspiration to empower your next steady step.

There is no right or wrong way to pray. (If you're uncomfortable with that term, then swap in a word that feels truer to you.) What I've come to know through my own experiences is that prayers are simply asks and wishes that you send out when you have surrendered, or at least suspended, the ego and are ready to admit that you don't know how, why, or what's next. Let's be real: if you knew what to do next and that it was all going to work out, you're probably not praying for it. Prayers may be uttered in the dark on your knees, during your yoga asanas, with your journal and your tea, or even out walking your dog (one of my personal faves). If you're religious, these prayers may take a prescribed form, but if you're not, you get to choose how you come into a state of surrender to be vulnerable with your wishes.

When you pray, you're asking for answers. You're wanting to understand your current life circumstances or how to propel yourself out of what you're experiencing into something more comfortable, abundant, and expansive. Through prayer and acknowledging the Divine, you're stepping into the realm of Water and Spirit, submerging yourself so that you can be suspended in the stillness. You let the excess – all those things that don't need to be there – wash away as you wait for the turn of the tide to begin moving you in the direction of your next steps.

I don't feel that prayer is simply throwing your arms in the air and proclaiming, "I give up" or "Do what you will with me." There has to be a part of you available to change, shift, and put in effort based on what is revealed to you. My prayer or manifestation practices have been way more successful when I'm willing to not just rely on the Divine to do all the heavy lifting and instead take responsibility for my side of the ask. I was first introduced to this concept when I was about 25, and I was ready to open myself up to a real relationship and meet my husband. The book *The Secret* was extremely popular around that time, and following its premise, I made this big list of all the things that I wanted in a partner and a man.

I shared it with someone I trusted, and her comment was, he sounds wonderful, but what are you going to bring to this relationship? I had never thought of it that way. But it quickly became apparent that it was equally important for me to have clarity on who I was and wanted to be in this relationship. So I went about journaling a new prayer, one where I spoke of the qualities that I was looking for and the characteristics that I found attractive, along with a paired statement about myself and what I would offer this man. When it was finished, I read it back, and it felt so much more grounded. I trusted it, I had faith in it, I could put my energy behind it. And I ended up being introduced to my now husband three days later. He's everything that I included in my prayer.

I have since done this same exercise in various ways, usually on walks with my dog around our neighborhood, where I have time to talk quietly to myself and the universe. My prayers were manifested in our dream house, which was aligned perfectly with what we needed in our lives at the time. I remember praying for our son before he was conceived, speaking about the ways I would foster his soul and why he should choose us and this life. I continue to pray in this way for even small things on a daily and monthly basis. No matter the ask, I always end it with: "I'm willing to do my part. Please show me the way."

Quite often the Divine will provide subtle invitations to clear and clean up different areas of your life either physically or energetically. A tension in a relationship will bubble up and require you to address it with a conversation. Physical clutter will irritate you, so you will need to clear it out of your home. You may notice you've been letting your routines and rituals slide and that you don't feel as connected to the Divine as you usually are. For me, one telltale sign is when I realize I've been muttering, "I'll figure it out on my own" – even though I know that statement isn't true and is only taking me further away from the deeper knowing within and the offerings of the Divine.

At times, clearing out the old can feel like you're taking one step forward, three steps backward, but I assure you, that isn't its purpose. By unearthing stories and patterns you no longer need, the soul can lessen the baggage you take with you on your next steps. Even if it feels like your prayers are going unanswered, keep showing up and doing the work. The answers will reveal themselves when they're ready for you to experience them.

Writing Prompts

What am I currently praying for? Get specific.

How can I show up to do my part?

Meditation: Inner Listening and Wu Wei

When we meditate, we let our minds drop into a yin state and rest. With practice, the stillness of meditation can be both comforting and an opportunity to develop our inner listening skills, so we can hear the whispers of our soul most connected to the wholeness of the universe.

I find that while prayer and meditation go hand in hand, it is wise to keep them as separate entities. In prayer, asks and wishes are usually projected toward possibilities that the mind can conceive. Meditation opens us up to realms of possibility we haven't yet encountered. Through it, we access our capacity to dream, while experiencing the safety of solitude and hopefully inner peace, so that we might pause and wait for serendipity to occur in its own divine timing.

To feel inner peace, we must be willing to surrender our attachments to the timelines and outcomes we perceive as in our best interest. Instead, we allow what is meant to be to come in its own divine time and way. In Chinese medicine this is referred to as Wu Wei (pronounced "woo way"), which can be translated as non-doing.

When you look at a yin-yang circle, Wu Wei is the line separating yin and yang, the dark from the light. (If your mind is blown, trust me, so was mine when I first learned of this in school.) In the context of the 5 Elements, Wu Wei dissects yin and yang from top to bottom, providing a direct connection between the Fire Element, which governs our desires, and the Water Element, where our soul resides. That little line, rarely given any thought, unites our desires with our soul, in order to bring forward epiphanies and inputs that can help direct our life path and purpose. However, because this all happens through non-doing, you can't force or will yourself to receive these insights.

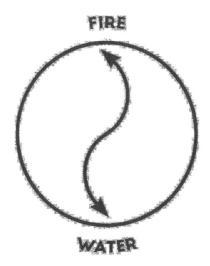

FIRE

WATER

Instead, you must rest your mind in meditation, be open, surrender the need to direct the energy, and release your expectations as to what will happen in this space. This means, too, letting go of the need for answers. Only then will you be available to receive the inputs or steady steps toward your destiny.

It's a tricky thing though, because you can't trick the universe into giving you what you want. You can't enter this space saying you surrender to whatever comes your way and still have your fingers crossed behind your back, hoping and praying that the answers you receive will give you exactly what you want. This is especially frustrating for Wood and Metal types, or type A individuals in general, who are used to getting their way or achieving what they set their minds to. The energetics of Water and its ability to undo plans can be more than a little unsettling. I've witnessed marriages come to an end and fertility patients come to their knees realizing that they may not get a baby at the end of this journey. I too have required a full course correction because I'd been traveling against the flow of my soul, thinking that my ego knew better.

However, if you're willing to put down your agenda and allow your mind to settle for even 10-20 minutes a day, there is magic and transformation available to you. Don't worry if sitting on a cushion with your eyes closed isn't accessible or desirable to you. If stillness only amplifies the questions and doubt, know that there are other ways that you can tap into meditation. You can move, walk, run, or color, for example; your Alchemy may nudge you toward another way.

Most Metals and Waters enjoy the practice of getting on a mat or cushion and practicing traditional meditation techniques. Woods may find it easier at first to move, allowing their mind to come to a resting place during a really good run or workout. I find that many of my Fire clients like to dance first and then come into a resting position. For the overthinking Earths, slow intentional movements like qigong or tai chi can be quite helpful to channel the mind. Guided meditations are also helpful as they allow your mind to rest on the words and invitations of another. Follow the inclinations of your mind and body to guide you to your unique meditation practice, and then devote time and attention to rest here often.

Writing Prompts

What feels like the most supportive way for me and my Alchemy to meditate?

Is it possible for me to carve out some time in my schedule to try this?

Intuition: Higher Guidance or Someone Else's Motives

Never before have we digested, integrated, and downloaded so much information. In this noisy world, everyone's vying for our attention so that we will buy in and follow them. But if we do so, it often comes at the expense of developing our own path, our own words, and our own motivation, and ignoring our intuition and the inner wisdom that will guide us to our destinies.

Multiple clients have asked me over the years, "How do I know if it's the universe and my intuition leading the way, or if I'm just listening to someone else's voice, someone much louder than me, who is saying all the right things for me to buy in when it's really not in my best interest? How do I know if I should jump into the unknown or stay the course?"

I'm sure you've had this same question. I certainly have. Let's face it, we've all had moments when it seemed like everything was lining up for us, the signs, other people cheering us on, and then it falls apart at the last minute or doesn't meet our expectations. As a result, our faith in ourselves gets chipped away a little more. What I've learned through my own experiences and leading others back to their inner knowing is that when you reference your Alchemy's core requirements (those of your dominant and secondary specifically), you can become more discerning and ask better questions about whatever you're considering.

If your requirements seem satisfied by a given direction, that's a good start. But you should look to satisfy the Water Element's core requirements too. Even if you're not a Water type or have zero Water in your chart, the questions provided by its core requirements will help hone your intuition beyond anything you've ever known. Once these have been reconciled, you will know with absolute clarity whether to leap with a soulful yes or put on the brakes with a sacred no.

Remember that the core requirements of Water are about safety, security, mediating risks, being authentic and feeling free. The ones that need your immediate attention are safety and security. These are often tied to our personal requirements of shelter, money, bodily autonomy, and typically anything to do with basic human needs. What these look like will be defined individually. The reason it's important to assess these requirements right away is because we won't feel free to leap into the unknown if we don't know how we're going to keep a roof over our head or feed ourselves and our family.

We cannot grow when we are in survival mode. Nature doesn't work this way, and neither do we. If you're feeling that your security and safety are constantly undermined, you have to first work toward having those needs met. This sometimes requires one to be vulnerable and ask for help, or it may necessitate jostling some other priorities, taking an eye off the big picture until the everyday necessities are sorted.

Each of us has a different definition of safety and security. For some, it's a particular dollar amount in a bank account; for others, it's knowing there's a couch to crash on if it all falls apart. Being truthful about what you need will be essential as you expand your capacity for greater things. Only then will you know when you're ready for the next step, and can move toward it with integrity.

After years of working with clients in this realm, I can tell you that once a person is able to assess the lowest level of safety and security they need, it's as if the heavens open up and a windfall of opportunity falls at their feet. This means it's incredibly worthwhile to be intimate with your personal definitions of safety and security. If your next direction in life is fraught with a lot of uncertainty, those core requirements of the Water Element need to be established and consolidated for you to trust yourself. You will then be able to engage with your own Element's core requirements as well as Waters to mediate the risks, work out the worst- and best-case scenarios, and assess if a particular opportunity is worth it to you.

Taking this step is like granting yourself a permission slip to really go for it. Once you've done this, you will feel free to be true to yourself and trust new beginnings that are authentic to who you are. You can know without a doubt that your values are reflected in a given opportunity (or if they're not, in which case it's better to let it go, knowing that you have even greater clarity on what you want and what it will feel like when it's a full embodied YES!). I tell my clients all the time that a lot of us have the same dreams, but they will look different based on our Element Alchemy and our personal definitions of our core requirements. This is how we know when something feels right, and that we aren't just adopting someone else's path, process, or even end result. You will know the difference when something feels like it was made for you.

Writing Prompts

What are my personal definitions of safety and security?

In what ways can I allow these definitions combined with my Alchemy's core requirements to help inform my intuition and decision-making?

Bypassing: Toxic Positivity

Fear is the prevailing emotion of the Water Element. No one likes to feel fearful, and navigating uncertainty and charting new paths that are different from the norm can be terrifying at times. One way we try to avoid fear is by overriding it with feelings of positivity. This inclination isn't inherently a bad thing. We can all use a silver lining in times that feel bleak or defeating. However, we must be careful that relentless positivity doesn't steal our ability to be present to the situation at hand. Projecting ourselves into a utopic future timeline is like being a tree with no roots. One gust of wind and it will swiftly topple to the ground. We don't need to drown in our sorrows or fears. And we don't need to construct storylines and identities around them that prevent us from growing or moving forward. But we also can't ignore them and pretend they're not there. Our emotions, especially those we most want to circumvent and not feel, have medicine in them.

To say to yourself, "Chin up," "Get over it," "It will get better," "Just be more positive," or "Sunnier days are just around the corner," when you are struggling, is to dismiss and minimize what you're going through. Even if a part of you believes that there are no coincidences and everything happens for a reason – and that it will ultimately all work out – at the moment you're suffering, it doesn't matter.

It's okay to feel sad, mad, fearful, or even lost. You are entitled to feel that way. Let yourself really feel it, then allow it to pass through your body and see what happens. If you're a person who tries not to express your emotions too often, or if the thought of allowing your feelings to flow is scary, know this. The average emotion moves through your body in about 90 seconds. What I'm saying is that if you connect to a raw emotion and allow it to move through your body unfiltered and without rumination, it's out of your system within 90 seconds. It often takes longer than this because our minds usually want to attach meaning and story to our emotions, but even then, most emotions will shift within 30 minutes to a few hours. The emotion that will stay longest in the body is sadness, and the average time that it takes to be felt and resolved is 120 hours or four days.[27]

Of course, there will be outliers, big life events in particular. Bereavement takes longer, especially when you factor in trauma and other life stressors that impact an individual's ability to process their emotions. What's important is that we allow for the expression and release of our emotions, instead of repressing them with ungrounded affirmations and fake positivity. We need to hold space to feel and to

---

[27] Verduyn, P., Lavrijsen, S. (2015). Which emotions last longest and why: The role of event importance and rumination. *Motiv Emot 39*, 119–127. https://doi.org/10.1007/s11031-014-9445-y

allow our emotions to just be what they are, without trying to fix or correct them, or shift ourselves away from them too quickly. It will take as long as it takes.

Your emotions carry wisdom. They're often a bridge connecting you to your essence and the source of your greater wisdom. When expressed often and freely, they can be one of your best barometers for what is actually happening. That gut feeling you get when you meet someone – perhaps they make you contract and feel fearful, or conversely put you at ease and feel joyful, as though you've known them a lifetime – this is your body's wisdom. Your emotions are amazing identifiers and can help confirm your intuition, but first you must be willing to feel them, so that you can become familiar with them and why they show up as they do.

Not only that but when we feel our emotions, rather than block them with forced affirmations muttered through clenched jaws and fists, everything becomes freer. Our minds clear, and we are able to connect with others in a more authentic way. Suddenly the solutions to our problems feel closer and within reach. When we're willing to feel the lows, we also get to feel the highs – true joy and embodied positivity.

Writing Prompts

When was the last time I honored my emotions and expressed them fully?

What feeling do I need to express right now?

Here are some ways to express your emotions using your body:

Bored, Anxious, Needing Grounding: YAWN
Sad or Grieving: CRY
Fearful or Anxious: SHAKE
Angry, Frustrated, Stuck: YELL or SCREAM
Happy, Joyful, Embarrassed, Ashamed: LAUGH

A *Love Letter* to Your Inner Water

Your soul and its quest for truth are as deep and as wide as the ocean. Your capacity to see the bigger picture of human experience and its evolution is ever expanding. Continue to dream, ask questions, and unlock the greater mysteries that you long to answer. If you become fearful or have doubts, know that your virtues of authenticity and integrity will always guide you beyond uncertainty and reveal to you the ways that your wisdom must be shared.

You have always been wise. Now it's time to trust yourself and everything that you know, as these are stepping stones to your becoming. Have faith in the power of the Divine to walk beside you as you put yourself out there in a way that feels good. Remember, you are free to create systems and foundations that serve you. You have your own ebb and flow to being and doing in the world. There is no rush, everything is divinely timed. Be assured that your efforts will sprout new seeds.

XO
Water

Chapter 12

Wood: Lifestyle & Livelihood

I Am Powerful

The Wood Element is active and emergent. Its upward yang-rising energetic assists us in devising steps and taking action to bring our visions into their realized form. The Wood Element shows up to help us stop fantasizing or merely talking about what we want, and actually make it happen. This energetic focuses us on outward expressions and our environment.

The more yin Elements we've previously discussed manifest internally, helping to foster our relationship with ourselves and our inner landscape. Many of their practices and invitations are unseen, and the shifts they create are subtle. In contrast, the actions of the yang expansive Elements of Wood and Fire are more visible. They expand our willingness to take up space and move toward our dreams and goals with greater expediency. That's not to say that they don't also invite us to come inward and cultivate equanimity, but the results of that work have outward manifestations. We tend to see their outcomes more immediately compared to our interactions with the more yin Elements.

I like to call Wood the "show-me-the-money Element," as this powerhouse governs the areas of our lifestyle and livelihood where our energy and emphasis are on career, money, possessions, travel, and goal setting. Here we often see the culmination and outward expression of the inner work facilitated by the yin Elements, as we seek to use our education, credibility, natural talents, along with our soul's mandate, to embody all aspects of ourselves to create a life that we love. Before this chapter, it may have been easy to view the different areas of our life as separate entities. The Wood Element allows us to see how they come together in relationship to one another and to our outside environment.

Through our career, and other outer manifestations of wealth and abundance, we connect to and reconcile our inner Wood's core requirements: empowerment, boundaries, growth and development, following truth, and having a vision. Feeling empowered encourages greater growth and development. With that growth, we discover our truth and create a vision that aligns with it, all while upholding sacred boundaries that expand our capacity to reach our goals and lead a meaningful life that is founded in love. To do this, the Wood energy helps us to get practical and strategic; while you may not have known the "how's" when you were dreaming in the Water phase, you will discover them in the Wood phase, where we seek to have our inner world reflected on the outside.

Work: Love What You Do, Do What You Love

To do work that you love, that's the dream, isn't it? To spend your days contributing in a way that aligns with your soul and uses your inherent strengths and gifts. Some individuals find themselves in this position, whether because they were lucky enough to be in the right place at the right time, or because they harnessed their inner Wood Element to propel them to their destination, stopping at nothing until they got there. However, the great majority of people are still searching for the secret of how to love what they do.

You might be tired of me saying this by now, but your Alchemy and your core requirements hold the keys to answering this question. Let's start by considering either your current position or a job you're interested in. Take a step back to look at it through the lens of the Elements. Who does this job feel best suited for? Is it the enthusiastic Fire that loves meeting people, collaborating and being center stage? Does it require the precision and organization of a Metal type, and would it satisfy their needs of having their talents appreciated and seeing a project through from inception to completion? Does it offer the opportunity to work alone or to set your own deadlines and productivity goals, the way a Water type prefers? Or are the deadlines strict, constantly making you feel behind and on a rocky foundation? Maybe this position or job needs a leader, one with a lot of Wood in their Alchemy, to direct, delegate and steer the project over the finish line. Or perhaps it's calling for a stable caretaker, an Earth type, who likes to hand-hold and create harmony by managing everyone else's drama?

We're conditioned to jump quickly at opportunity, in fear that if we don't, we'll lose our chance. Applying an Elemental lens to a job or type of work offers us a chance to slow down and ask better questions so we can know wholeheartedly if it's right for us. Of course, because we have all the Elements within us, we can call on our less dominant Elements to perform the necessary tasks, even if they're not truly in our skill set or comfort zone. But do you want to? Every hour of every day for weeks and years on end?

The answer to this question comes from looking at your individual Alchemy's core requirements, as these are the needs that must be reconciled to love your work. Checking in with these requirements will also help you confirm whether you should view a gig as a short-term opportunity to tide you over until something better comes along, or as a long-term prospect that will evolve with you to generate bigger and greater things. How aligned your requirements are to your work will largely determine the quality of life that you will experience while in that role, or with that company or project. Armed with this information, you have a choice: to go forward as is, negotiate terms that will better support you, or walk away. As per my earlier comment, you can assess your current job through this lens as well, noticing what parts of your Alchemy are supported and which ones aren't. You can then use this to start a conversation about how you might feel more valued and enthusiastic to show up each day. If you work for yourself, you get to decide what changes to make to avoid burnout and resentment.

Now of course, sometimes our soul's mandate requires a course correction, taking us on a completely different path than that which we have traveled thus far. Then what? First and foremost, ensure the requirements for safety and security that you defined in the Water chapter remain intact. If that means that you can't just up and quit, then it's a matter of building a bridge from where you are to where you want to be. To do this successfully, you must get really purposeful with your actions and stay patient as you take small steps daily that help to move the needle forward. First, you have to know what you want. If you're unsure, you may need to return to the Water Element, spending time in meditation and prayer to access greater clarity. Once you know what you think you want to do, then you can begin to map out and strategize what's required to get closer to that possibility. There will come a time when you will have to leap and leave the job that's helped provide safety and security; however, by that point, your intuition and your core requirements will be largely satisfied and you will feel confident that you will make it to the other side.

Writing Prompts

What job description best supports my Alchemy and core requirements?

Can this be created in the job I have now? If so, how?

If not, are there other opportunities that better support my gifts?

Can I build a bridge to help make one of them a reality?

Money: Yin, Yang and Abundance

Are you a spender or a saver? Another way to put this is, are your interactions with money more yin or yang? Personally, I prefer the latter question; there is less judgment attached to it, and it provides a better opportunity to reflect on your relationship to money and make changes to it if you wish. Yin and yang are two sides of the same whole; by using them as a framework, we can hold space and intention to be both, acknowledging that there are times in our life when we are more yin and times when we are more yang when it comes to money. Neither is better than the other, although too great an imbalance can cause problems.

Our yin interactions with money are more stable. Through them, we create the intention to fix and consolidate money by placing it in some kind of container, through assets, holdings, and savings. In these places our money rests, so to speak, and appreciates and increases in value.

Money is more active and moveable in our yang interactions with it. This is the money we spend on experiences, relationships, life. We use it to participate in the world and to connect to all the areas of life governed by the other Elements. When we allow ourselves to view money through a yang lens, we can think about how we wish to use it, and in this way give the money we generate a greater purpose or resonance. The ever-practical Wood type knows that you need to be able to pull together what you need to achieve your goals, and money is one of the ingredients. Like all things governed by the Wood Element, vision, planning, and empowerment need to be part of the equation for money to reach its intended potential. Identify the purpose of your money, and your decisions and opportunities will begin to match your intentions.

Because yin and yang are interdependent and not separate, there are going to be times in our life when we are more yang with our money. We may need to use, or even borrow, it to fuel our desires for greater education, fund our experiences, travel, acquire material possessions, and meet our requirements for self-care. Then there are going to be times when we feel called to be more yin, slowing down the flow of money going out, possibly being more frugal and saving what isn't required for necessities. We may swing from one side to the other at different times of our life, eventually finding a sweet spot where we can hold space for both.

To realize your individual sweet spot requires honoring your Alchemy. I have found that most people spend money to help meet their core requirements. Earths seek to feel supported and nourished, Metals to be in positions that allow for recognition and appreciation, Waters to feel safe, secure but also free, Fires to create opportunities for closeness and intimacy, and Woods to generate greater growth and development in the direction of their vision. Prioritizing where your money is best allocated to support you in feeling whole and at ease provides a basis for choosing whether to spend or save your money, and can empower you to engage in activities, offerings and positions that generate the money that you require to make your desires a reality.

What I love about using your Alchemy and the paradigm of yin and yang to better understand your relationship to money is that it provides you the freedom to set aside other people's judgments, because you're intentionally choosing what you're doing. It may look odd or irresponsible to someone else; in fact, that's likely, because their core requirements and Alchemy are directing them in a different direction and determining which frequency – yin or yang – they wish to engage. But that doesn't mean it's wrong for you. This perspective may also provide much-needed resolve and self-forgiveness for those times when you feel you didn't act with full integrity and perhaps spent beyond your means.

We can also take this understanding further by extending it to our partner, spouse, colleagues, etc. Taking into account each other's Alchemies and core requirements can build a stronger bridge, where both individuals' needs and requirements for the money they generate can support each in creating the best possible outcomes.

Writing Prompts

Identify different times in your life when your interactions with money were more yang.

Identify different times in your life when your interactions with money were more yin.

What is my ideal interaction with money now, and how does that best support my Alchemy and core requirements?

Travel: Adventure Awaits

Stepping away from the everyday to experience something new can be just what we need to gain a fresh perspective. Adventure and travel are excellent ways to foster alternative ways of thinking and an appreciation for our current life's path. We broaden our horizons through experiencing different environments, cultures, and ways of living. The Wood Element within each of us delights in the opportunity to see what else is out there, whether it's halfway around the world or the next town over.

Routine and structure may be a comfort for some Element types; however, we can all benefit from being a little bit more flexible and leaning into new environments. By doing this, you may gain new information that inspires a vision for where you want to go next; this can act as a catalyst for events that bring you to a life or destination you could have never conceived of had you just stayed home.

For those who can't imagine a life without travel, you might be compelled to start looking at flights and dream destinations right now. If that's true, do it. Even if you can't take that trip until some time in the future, the very act of seeking new directions creates shifts within our energetic field that help us look at life's obstacles differently. The Wood type and the Wood Element within each of us require growth and development; we need to feel as though we are moving forward with direction and conviction. Without this feeling, things get heavy, stagnant, and difficult to navigate; we can't see the forest through the trees. Being willing to step outside of the ordinary influences the way the Wood Element manifests within us, helping us to remain open to the possibility of new ideas and different paths that can lead to solving problems we experience in our everyday lives.

If the idea of sleeping in different beds and living out of a suitcase makes you shudder, this too is perfectly okay. Adventure doesn't necessarily mean that you need to jet off to other cities and countries. Instead, you can use this area of your life as an invitation to try something new in your own community. Give yourself permission to explore nature and experience the beauty and magic of the outdoors. Walk a different route, hike a trail that leads you to your new favorite spot, visit the lake, ocean, mountains, or desert, whatever is nearby, and spend an hour taking in different scenery. Whatever you do, allow it to reset your nervous system and open you up to the greater opportunities that are available to you. Anything is possible when you're willing to step into new environments and be flexible and available to moments of serendipity.

Writing Prompts

Where do I feel called to visit?

Plan your adventure. What are you going to do, see and experience?

Possessions: The Outer Expression of Wealth

The Wood Element is a visual Element. It represents the culmination and expression of all your inner work. Think of the sprout that shoots up from the soil to begin the part of its journey where it is visible to the outside world. This is what possessions are: aspects of your values, requirements and Alchemy brought into physical form. This category under Wood's governance could be divided further into subcategories, such as the house you live in, the clothes you wear, the car you do or don't drive, and the trinkets and material possessions you own. Each of us have a unique relationship to these categories based on varying degrees of value and need.

As with our relationship to money, I find that it's important to take note of our inner commentary or assumptions about what are "good" or "bad" possessions. We can feel quite righteous in our attitudes about this area of our life and judge others' choices, when in fact it really doesn't matter. If we live in accordance with our Alchemy and let others do the same, we will each find right relationship within ourselves and with the possessions with which we do or don't surround ourselves. Not everyone wants a house on the beach or the latest and greatest gadget, but there's nothing wrong with you if you do.

The question to ask yourself is, what's important to me, and is that reflected in the possessions I have? For some people, it's designer clothes, expensive cars, and big houses, and for others it's not. In fact, you might have all those things but come to realize that none of them reflect the life you want to create. I have had a lot of conversations with Wood types who say to me that navigating this area of their life is confusing, and they have started to doubt that they are a Wood type at all. If their type is governed by the "show-me-the-money" Element, are they supposed to want "all of the things"? For many of them, this just doesn't feel true. I would reiterate, that is absolutely okay. When this question arises, I simply invite them to take a step back and notice their associations to wealth, abundance, and ownership. We each need to figure out what that is for ourselves, instead of taking on conditioning and definitions that society imposes. Having it all might just mean meeting your needs and buying or investing in products that align with your values and what you deem important. That feels pretty abundant to me.

Having permission to examine and allow yourself to want what you want is powerful. When I ask my clients what they actually want in their life, they often have trouble giving voice to their desires. More often than not, we spend our mental bandwidth thinking of things we don't want, which feels heavy and stagnant for the Wood energetic. Engaging its potential for expansion and visioning is necessary. This is why creating a vision board can be an excellent exercise to help facilitate greater clarity on what you need and want in your life. In some ways, this may feel similar to the dreaming and prayers discussed in the chapter on the Water Element; however, there are small discernible differences. The main one is that this is a visual exercise, which further engages the Wood energetic as it also governs our eyesight in Chinese medicine.

Naturally your vision board will encompass far more than just material things. It may speak to the quality of your relationships and areas of life governed by the other Elements. Don't worry. Put it all on the page, as this further emphasizes how the Elements and the other areas of our life support each other in right relationship. If you're lacking clarity on what you actually want versus what you feel is appropriate or suitable to want, I invite you to spend some time with your Alchemy and look closely at your dominant Element, perhaps your secondary, and your core requirements. How would they be further supported by inviting certain things, experiences, and relationships into your life? By honoring your requirements, you give your vision roots and make it sustainable, so it can become a reality. You may need to journal or go for a walk in your favorite neighborhood to gain inspiration or to help guide you. Then take those ideas and put them into visual form, which will act as a reminder and help hone your goals and soulful strategy to begin the process of walking toward them.

Writing Prompts

How do my current material possessions or visual manifestations of my wealth and abundance reflect my Alchemy's core requirements?

What else do I want in the form of material possessions or visual manifestations of my wealth and abundance?

How are they supported by my Alchemy's core requirements?

Vision Boarding with the Elements

If creating a vision board is new to you, here are some instructions to get you started.

1) Gather magazines, words, pictures, colorful pens, art supplies and a large piece of poster board. There are no rules, and you may use whatever inspires you to get a little crafty. If crafts aren't your thing, you may also do this digitally by creating a file of pictures or a board of pins. You can hide this so nobody else can see it on an app like Pinterest.

2) Revisit your Alchemy, paying close attention to your dominant and

perhaps your secondary Element. What qualities about yourself do you want to enhance or feel in a physical form? Looking back to your answers to questions about how you wish to experience your core requirements, are there particular things, experiences, or relationships that you would like to welcome into your life to support them?

3) Reflect on all five life areas that the 5 Elements govern (I realize we have yet to get into relationships, but you can still spend some time envisioning those in this exercise). What do you want these areas to look like in your future life?

4) Next, get crafting by finding meaningful images that reflect your vision. You can even draw them or write words or prose, as these are still visual representations. You will be looking at this every day for a few minutes to remind yourself of the life you want to create.

5) Spurred by Water's mindfulness, you can then begin to watch for signs and places that are calling you to act and that will take you closer to this dream.

Goal Setting: Small Steps Lead to Great Distances

Being able to envision the big picture is awesome and necessary for the empowerment of the Wood Element. However, the genius of this Element is that it helps us break the big stuff down and get really clear on each small step that's required to accomplish our goals. Water holds space for seeing the bigger picture, but Wood helps uncover the how's. It supports us as we tackle one step at a time, or better yet, delegate some or all of them to someone else. Don't forget about Wood's ability to activate leadership.

Often when we realize what our greater goals and dreams are, we can get overwhelmed, paralyzed by all that needs to happen to achieve them. But the trick is to slow down the pace a little bit and make the decision to take one action. If the overwhelming feeling persists, it's often because that single step still feels more like a leap and it needs to be broken down even further.

This is the magic the Wood Element offers you once you get clear about what you want. The seedling doesn't become a grand oak overnight. Of course not. It starts with a stem and two little leaves, then it gets a little taller and the stem gets a little thicker, and then the two leaves become four and then taller, thicker, denser, and eventually that tender stem starts to resemble bark and those first leaves become branches, which bud their own leaves. With each inch that it grows, that seedling gains more evidence and confidence that it's going to become that tall awe-inspiring oak.

Your dreams and visions take form the same way. They take root and make it to the light with every task or action that you complete. Each time you show up for yourself and complete the steps as they appear, you strengthen your confidence, drive, and conviction in your vision. If you don't plan for your dreams to come true, they won't. They will remain fantasy without form.

So, first things first, get out a pen and paper, and list all the steps that need to happen to get from where you are to where you want to be. This is required for every goal you set, from running a marathon, writing a book, starting a business, losing weight, to getting your master's degree.

Ask yourself questions to gain greater clarity on what is going to be required to get the job done. How long is this going to take? What materials if any do you need? Do you need coaching or support to help you get there? Does your family or partner need to be on board to cheerlead you and talk you down from quitting when you hit a snag in your plans or execution? Naturally some Element types will be more adept and willing to answer these questions, i.e. Metal and Wood, whereas other types may want to take things as they go, remaining a little more noncommittal and open to diversions if they show up. This too can work out; however, there is medicine here for you if you're willing to engage your inner Wood Element to support you in making changes that will get you closer to embodying the life and accomplishments you desire.

When the bigger picture is broken down into the work that needs to be done, it's way easier to get going, be productive, and actually see your vision take shape.

Once you have the steps and timeline figured out, take the opportunity to acknowledge what is in your zone of genius and what's not. This is key. We are so conditioned to thinking and feeling as though we have to do it all ourselves, and that's just not true. Look for examples of strong leaders – a lot of them Wood types – and notice their ability to delegate so that they may continue doing what they do best. Identifying which steps are going to be a struggle allows you to notice where you may need help and support. If you can afford or have the resources to outsource some things on your list, do that. Or there may be an opportunity to think outside of the box to access the help and support you require. If this won't work, that's okay too. I invite you to lengthen the deadline a smidge to ease the expectations you have for yourself. This will make this journey of execution far more enjoyable, and you will have the time to figure out each step as it happens. J. C. R. Licklider wrote, "People overestimate what can be done in a year and underestimate what can be done in ten." If fully realizing your dream takes a few extra weeks or months than you originally intended, would you be any less proud?

The next step is getting your plan into your calendar. When I was a national competitive ice dancer, every spring I would sit down with my partner and my coach to plan out our entire season. We would list the objectives of each week until Nationals the following year. Then we would include everything, from which competitions we were intending to compete at, what our goal was for placement at Nationals, when programs needed to be choreographed, when costumes needed to be completed and by who, what off-ice activities would be most beneficial to us, and the schedule of when we would train, when we would taper, etc. No detail was too small; it all went into the training log. This exercise helped us in so many ways, allowing us to hold space for our big dreams for our overall competitive career, while creating actionable steps for us to see and believe that our goals could happen, and providing accountability to keep us on the right track, week in and week out. Following these steps, we created greater evidence that our goals were achievable.

When you're putting all your steps and stages into your calendar, make sure the other Elements are represented in your timetable. Ensure you have time for self-care, creativity, dreaming and relationships alongside your desired project. In the bonus section (www.ashleyabbs.com/5elementalchemy-resources), there are calendars and planning materials available to assist you in being supported by the Elements so that your goals can come into form.

Writing Prompts

What goals do I want to pursue?

What are all the steps required to allow me to accomplish my goals?

What supports do I require to help me get there?

Tunnel Vision: Wood Overacting on Earth

The Wood energy can be pretty commanding. Our Western culture idolizes it, and we can all find ourselves feeling the pressure to perform and value this one particular Element and its area of life's governance as the almighty. When this happens, often at no fault of our own, we come out of right relationship with the other Elements and their areas of life, emphasizing our lifestyle and livelihood over everything else. Usually the Element that gets neglected the most is Earth and our capacity for self-care.

In Chinese medicine we call this Wood overacting on Earth. It's a fairly common syndrome that we see in clinic. The Wood Element and its energies have taken over and clouded out Earth's ability to be supported or nourished. This occurs in part because the Wood energy is stronger and more yang than the Earth's yin energy; if given the opportunity, it will always take over and become root bound if there isn't adequate earth to sustain it, which will eventually result in it becoming undernourished and burned out.

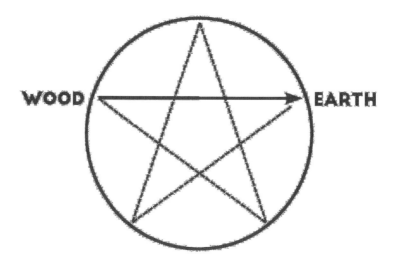

In the beginning, this warping of our relationship with the Elements is subtle. We simply skip the run at lunch because there's a big deadline to meet; we eat at our desk or skip meals altogether because we're just too focused or busy with a project. Eventually we find ourselves sliding down the slippery slope to where this is the norm. We consciously or unconsciously assert the belief that the other energetics and their activities or relationships are less important or can wait. Naturally the impetus for this doesn't have to be paid work; our self-care and other requirements related to the Earth Element can easily be put on hold for just about anything – housework, laundry, dishes and other daily tasks that seem to never end. And yet we tell ourselves that when they're done, then we'll take care of our own needs.

It may not be your self-care and the Earth Element that take a backseat to Wood. Any of the Elements and their areas of life can be commandeered by the Wood Element and its energetics. What areas get shoved aside likely point back to your Alchemy in some way, in wanting to find confirmation of your greatest need: the belief that you are enough, worthy, safe, loveable, and powerful. We have been conditioned to believe that these requirements can be fulfilled through our actions. But no, they are innate truths that require no action other than the belief in oneself and in one's connection to their soul's knowing.

In fact, your work and vision will be more whole, more centered and supported when the other areas of your life are given attention and enjoyed. Together let's compassionately detach from being too busy and too stressed, and from believing that something or someone is more important than ourselves and our needs. In doing so, we surrender conditioning and learned beliefs that link our self-worth and getting our own needs met with the satisfaction and success of the people and companies that we serve.

How do you know when Wood is overacting on your Earth or other Elements?

- You have abandoned self-care.
- You've put off taking time to participate in ritual or supportive circles.
- You press pause on your dreams for "when I have time."
- You start to ignore your heart's call. Your intuition isn't speaking to you, or if it is, you refuse or are too distracted to tune in.
- There's no Wu Wei or flow, only force, "willpower," and control.
- You're operating from the belief that your ability to be enough, worthy, loveable, safe, or empowered is dependent on what you "DO" for a living and not an innate truth.

Writing Prompts

When in the past have I allowed my work to crowd out the other areas of life?

When this happens, what suffers?

What structure can I put in place to remind me that the other areas of life need attention even when I have lots of work to get done?

A *Love Letter* to Your Inner Wood

Ambition aligned with your truthful heart is your superpower. Find your feet, stand tall, and lead. Stay committed to growing and putting yourself out there; your efforts will come back to you tenfold in the form of opportunity and abundance. If you're feeling stuck, ask for support. You don't have to do everything by yourself. There's a team waiting for you to lead them so that they too can do their part in making the world a better place.

You are a trailblazer; you're tenacious, ingenious and incredibly benevolent. Have faith in your ability to envision a future life of love and legacy. Allow soulful strategy to guide you, offering you course corrections so you can bend when you need to while still reaching for the light. Set your sights on the horizon and begin to put one foot in front of the other. Keep going, don't back down from what you know is true. Believe in yourself because I believe in you.

XO
Wood

Chapter 13

Fire: Relationships & Service

I Am Loved

The Fire Element resides at the highest yang point of the circle and is considered closest to the realms of the heavens, including the sun, moon, and stars. Its symbolism is represented through metaphors related to heat, expansion and light. It has also been represented as a blossoming flower, opening itself up so that its beauty can be witnessed by the world. Our inner Fire is expressed when we open our hearts, fully express ourselves, and connect with our environment through our participation in relationships, community and acts of service.

As is the case with the Wood Element, working with and healing the Fire Element brings about expedient changes to our outer world. Fire is a catalyst for transformation. Not only that but because the Fire Element inspires us to connect to our heart and love for ourselves and others, it can exponentiate our impact and potential legacy.

The Fire Element governs the areas of life that encompass our relationships and acts of service. All relationships from romantic, work, family, friends, and supportive circles fall under one big umbrella here, although obviously they have their own nuances and require unique navigation. Fire also offers opportunity for us to foster our participation in community, play, celebration, and philanthropy. Each of these areas opens up a different level of our heart, teaching us to be flexible and available to living a life that we love.

Through connection with Fire's core requirements – to experience both the giving and receiving of love and affection, as well as closeness, emotional stability, happiness, and commitment – we access Fire's warmth and uplifting positivity, which draws others closer to us and us to them. By melting away some of our inhibitions and protecting walls, Fire promotes greater vulnerability and weaves joy, laughter, and moments of spontaneity into our daily life. It encourages us to live for the moment at hand and savor what's available. And its energies feed on themselves, inciting even more opportunities to expand our circle of influence and create a soulful impact that will linger like embers.

Relationships: The Merging of Alchemies

Relationships are a merging or marrying of Alchemies. When we form a relationship, we seek connection and to be seen, heard and understood authentically. In this way, relationships can serve as playgrounds or laboratories where we experiment with who we are and what we like, as well as what we don't. Over time, we learn to make better choices about who we let in to see our more vulnerable side and who doesn't get that privilege. Relationships also provide us the opportunity to develop discernment and self-awareness of our motivations. After all, we decide who we want to have relationships with. This is true for all types of relationships: romantic, friendship, a supportive circle, colleagues and even family. While these relationships types may have different boundaries and varying levels of intimacy, we still get to choose how we show up and interact with the other individuals involved.

When it comes to the Element types, there isn't one almighty relationship combination. In Taoism and the 5 Elements, there are always opportunities to seek equanimity and right relationship by observing one's motivations and core requirements as they intertwine with another's. The 5 Element philosophy defines relationships as being of three types. They can be synergistic through the generating cycle, antagonizing through the control cycle, and the third type is when two Elements are the same. While the terms may suggest one type is better than another, that is simply untrue. Each relationship type, like any relationship, involves work to keep it on course and cycling properly. This means both individuals must be responsible to themselves and their own inner work, while also creating opportunities for connection and deeper intimacy for their relationship to evolve.

Before you read about the different relationship dynamics, I would like to preface this by saying these are generalized examples. Naturally, relationships are much more intricate and nuanced than what can be captured in a bulleted summary. Also, you are not just your dominant Element; the rest of your Alchemy will cumulatively determine how you seek reconciliation of your core requirements in your relationships, as will the Alchemy of the other person. So, while you may experience an epiphany or find resonance in an explanation, as it relates to one or more of your relationships, it's important to not hold too tightly to what you learn. These are not laws written in stone. People evolve, and in relationships, that evolution is accelerated. We are pushed and supported to reclaim our wholeness and achieve greater self-awareness quickly to allow for deeper connection, communion and even resolution to the more troublesome aspects of our relationships. It is also important to remember that life experience, trauma, and stressors, factors at times out of our control, also play a role in our relationships. These can warp our interactions or highlight a need for healing. Tread softly as you remember past experiences where you allowed your heart to be vulnerable enough to love.

In the sections that follow, I have teased apart each of the Element relationship types so that you can see the pair's synergistic qualities, points of friction, and an accompanying supportive energetic. When I refer to synergistic qualities, I am speaking of the ways Element types might support one another by enhancing or appreciating each other's personal strengths. Points of friction are annoyances and sources of frustration that can be attributed to a certain combination of Element types. Finally, supportive Elements are those not in the primary relationship that may act as an outside support. These supportive Elements are stabilizers, helping to hold the dominant Elements in relationship. This can work in various ways. For example, two people in a relationship may employ the medicine of the stabilizing Element through mindfulness and exercises that allow its support to be felt and its requirements met. Alternatively, they may want to bring in a third party in the form of a friend or therapist who has a predominance of that stabilizing Element to help ensure right relationship and a healthy union.

Use the following writing prompts to support you as you identify the different relationships you've experienced in the past and currently experience in the present.

Writing Prompts

What Element types have I had relationships with in my past? Currently?

In each of my past relationships how were my strengths and heart supported?

In each of my past relationships where did I experience points of friction?

In my current relationships, how are my strengths supported?

In my current relationships, where do I experience points of friction?

In my current relationships, how may I incorporate the supportive energetic to help the relationship grow and reach new levels of appreciation and intimacy?

The Generating Cycle of Relationships

The generating cycle is represented by the clockwise direction of the 5 Element chart. In it, one Element generates the next. In the ancient texts this relationship is seen as Earth bears Metal, Metal collects Water, Water nourishes Wood, Wood feeds Fire, and Fire makes Earth. This cycling of the Elements is considered supportive because each one helps to support and nurture the next to reach its potential. This is not to say that there aren't edges or potential for conflict in these relationships.

Each individual still seeks to confirm their requirements and be both seen and understood, which naturally can cause tension.

Earth and Metal

Synergistic Qualities
- Both have even temperaments and avoid drama.
- Earth nurtures Metal through their compassion, loyalty, and ability to create a bridge for Metal to experience greater ease in the company of others.
- Metal protects Earth by helping them detach from their worries, shift old patterns, and move beyond their comfort zone. They also help distill their ideas into form and create a connection to their purpose.
- Earth often looks to Metal as a mentor or teacher due to their expertise and wisdom.

Points of Friction
- Earth can become insecure and overwhelmed by Metal's tendency for righteousness and control.
- Metal can feel suffocated and yearn to detach when Earth's insecurities and neediness result in them over-nurturing and caretaking.
- They have different preferences for sharing and receiving affection: Earth easily provides warm and physical touch, whereas Metal prefers less overt expression.

Supportive Energetic
Fire: Introduces warmth and joy to inspire spontaneity and shake up routines to melt Metal and ground Earth in the present moment.[28]

---

[28] The "synergistic qualities," "points of friction" and "supportive energetics" in the descriptions of the Element relationship types have been drawn from

Metal and Water

Synergistic Qualities

- This is a meeting of the minds. These relationships are often founded on deep friendship. Both are known to devour books, ideas and wisdom.
- The Water type, being the dreamer and thinker, and the Metal, who is the organized strategist, together can bring ideas into form rather easily.
- Metal assists Water in detaching, focusing, and bringing ideas and projects to completion.
- Water inspires Metal to dream bigger, beyond what they see, as well as to let loose, abandon their agenda every now and then, and go with the flow.

Points of Friction

- Metals are neat and tidy, and prefer to keep everyone in order and organized.
- Waters are less concerned with order; they tend to be somewhat messy and okay with clutter. This quality can drive a Metal mad, and if they aren't able to reach a compromise, this can be their undoing.
- Metals can feel abandoned or ghosted by Waters who often need to get lost and be unavailable; this can occur at a moment's notice with no previous planning.
- Water will at times struggle with Metal's discipline and rigidity, leading them to feel trapped in a direction or situation that no longer feels authentic.

The Five Elements by Dondi Dahlin (2016), as well as observations made in my professional practice.

Supportive Energetic

Earth: Can provide a supportive foundation to inspire each individual to take care of their own needs through self-care and to facilitate a meeting in the middle where harmony can be created.

Water and Wood

Synergistic Qualities

- This is a good combination for converting ideas to action. The collaboration of the Water's dreamer qualities with the Wood's driven actionable nature often results in great things being created.
- Water supports Wood to slow down and go with the flow, demonstrating how taking the foot off the gas can result in greater opportunities and information to inspire goals beyond what was first envisioned.
- Wood helps Water emerge with greater conviction to be productive and meet deadlines. With Wood's leadership, Waters can walk alongside their ideas as they manifest into form.

Points of Friction

- If feeling pushed beyond the limits of their integrity or what feels authentic, Water will retreat and abandon the directions that Wood has put in place.
- Water can struggle with Wood's constant need to be productive and doing something. It is wise for Water to carve out time to be in stillness and solitude.
- Wood can become frustrated with Water's wishy-washy, at times noncommittal energy.
- Wood can grow tired of trying to navigate Water's pace, the back-and-forth and need for long discussions, when they are more adept at moving forward and gaining momentum.

Supportive Energetic

Metal: Provides opportunity for moments of gratitude to assist both Water and Wood to come back to their purpose and their "why."

Wood and Fire

Synergistic Qualities

- Wood supports Fire to stay on task, focus, and create sustainable desires and sparks of inspiration.
- Wood assists Fire to form appropriate boundaries and create soulful strategy to allow them to manifest their desires into reality. They also support Fire to keep going when their interest is starting to wane.
- Fire inspires Wood to play, celebrate, and experience spontaneity and joy. Fire encourages Wood to let off steam and lessen the pressures they have imposed on themselves.
- Fire supports Wood to relax and savor the moment they are currently in, rather than wait until some date in the projected future when the work is complete.

Points of Friction

- Wood can tire of a Fire's drama.
- Wood can become frustrated with the non-linear way that a Fire thinks and works. They want more straightforward, actionable steps, and this often goes against Fire's genius.
- Fire can struggle with the timelines, details, and endurance of a Wood type, especially if there is little time set aside for fun and play.
- Fire might feel their light dim and their sparks fizzle when continually confronted with the reality check of all the actions and steps required to make their desires possible. It is wise for Wood to listen and not always play devil's advocate when a Fire is expressing their ideas; often those ideas that aren't

meant to be will be snuffed out on their own without any of Wood's objections.

Supportive Energetic

Water: Both Wood and Fire, due to their yang nature, tend to always be out and about, networking and collaborating to accelerate their expansion. Water supports both energetics to slow down and come inward so that they can bring greater authenticity and integrity to support their gifts and their actions.

Fire and Earth

Synergistic Qualities

- These types form relationships founded on love, support and pleasure.
- Fire's warmth and ability to inspire fun and laughter assist Earth to get out of their head, release worry, and be present to the here and now.
- Fire's spontaneity and love of trying something new can shake up an Earth's routine and break through any ruts they may be experiencing.
- Earth, through their support and stability, helps to calm and relax Fire, inviting them to consolidate and ground their energies to ensure they don't burn out.
- An Earth's loyalty and compassion allow a Fire to be seen as they are, and give them a break from always needing to perform and be on.

Points of Friction

- This relationship can become highly codependent.
- Fire can feel suffocated and smothered by Earth's tendency to caretake.

- Due to an Earth's worries or judgments, Fire may find themselves less willing to put themselves out there and can feel their light and spark dulled or snuffed out.
- Earth can tire of Fire's drama and unpredictable swings from high to low. This results in them feeling overwhelmed by everything they feel they need to hold space for.
- Earth can tire of Fire's need to be the center of attention. This is further exacerbated if Earth is in denial about wanting greater attention and support.

Supportive Energetic

Wood: Given a Fire's tendency to seek fun, pleasure and enjoyment combined with Earth's desire to stay in their comfort zone, this relationship can get very complacent. Fueling it with a bit of direction and visioning can help them to move forward with some of their desires and ideas.

The Control Cycle in Relationships

Together, the lines that create the star within the circle of Elements is referred to as the control cycle. These lines represent antagonizing relationships. Here, we experience directed energy that can either restrain us or push us to adapt and evolve due to greater pressure. In the traditional sense, these relationships are explained as Water has the capacity to extinguish Fire, Fire to melt Metal, Metal chops Wood, Wood parts Earth (as its roots or trees can prevent soil erosion), and Earth dams, muddies or absorbs Water. This cycle often has a negative connotation to it; however, a lot of positive occurrences can happen within these types of relationships, as they help to catalyze growth and evolution.

In these types of relationships, it's important that each individual has autonomy. It is likely that you won't have the same interests, hobbies, etc., and that's okay. Naturally, there will be common ground and areas of overlap; however, you may not be the couple – or the friends or colleagues – glued at the hip, doing everything together. In my experience, individuals in these relationships have the deficient aspects of their Element type and Alchemy challenged (referenced in the summary of each Element type chapter under opportunities for growth), so it's important that each person is responsible for their own core requirements. This way everyone feels secure in their independence, while still nurturing their relationship.

Water and Fire

Synergistic Qualities
- Fire feels supported by the big dreamy ideas of Water.
- Fire is inspired by Water (and their sense of freedom) to embrace being themselves and not always performing.

- Water helps Fire slow down and appreciate mellow activities that allow them to come inward to themselves and their own intuition, rather than looking for approval.
- Water enjoys the excitement, enthusiasm and warmth of Fire's love and energy.

Points of Friction

- Water is more prone to being a homebody and requires lots of alone time to think, dream and contemplate. Fire is a social butterfly with a full calendar.
- If a Fire succumbs to a Water's tendencies, they will become isolated and depressed, losing their fire and ability to affirm desires.
- Water will be disappointed if required to be Fire's arm candy and sidekick for social events. This creates feelings of low self-esteem and abandonment, as they oscillate between being needed and being a third wheel.
- Water can struggle with Fire's superficiality and desire to meet other's approval and applause, and see these tendencies as inauthentic.

Supportive Energetic

Earth: A place to meet in the middle, Earth inspires Fire to come home, recharge and look inward, while creating a safe container for Water to create moments for intimacy and connection.

Fire and Metal

Synergistic Qualities

- Fire is heart-centered, expressive and emotional, whereas Metal is more pragmatic, rational, and doesn't always articulate their emotions in words, expressions or gestures.

- Fire melts Metal by helping them to loosen up and invite a bit of dis-order and spontaneity into their lives, helping them break free of rigid routines.
- Metal inspires Fire to slow down, deepen their capacity for listening and become present.
- Their union has the potential to be playful, fun, and full of reverence and purpose, provided they are willing to acknowledge that they have different preferences for expression and implementation.

Points of Friction

- Fire can view themselves as inferior to Metal in terms of intellect and requirements for perfection.
- Metal's self-esteem can bottom out if they believe they are unworthy of a Fire's love and affection. This can prompt them to detach and cut themselves off to ensure self-preservation.
- Fire can struggle with Metal's detachment and can reciprocate by shutting the doors of their heart and closing off their exuberance to protect themselves.

Supportive Energetic

Water: This energetic invites Fire to come inward to cultivate greater self-awareness, while assisting Metal to let go and relax into the flow of the moment.

Metal and Wood

Synergistic Qualities

- Both are disciplined, enjoy structures, and are powerful.
- Metal is able to recognize a Wood's strengths and articulate and affirm them.
- Wood allows Metal to feel seen through words of encouragement, meaningful connection, and friendship.

- Together, Wood's leadership and vision combined with Metal's ability to organize ensure the completion of a goal or project.

Points of Friction

- Power struggles persist when both believe that they are right and are unwilling to compromise on their viewpoint or perspective.
- In this situation, Wood gets angry and frustrated. Metal detaches and cuts off.
- They can find themselves competing against one another, taking on all the responsibilities and trying to prove the other one wrong.
- Image, posturing and perfection can create a superficiality to this union, where both parties are more concerned with what it looks like than what it really is.

Supportive Energetic

Fire: Fire's warmth, joy and lightness are supportive to both these types, as they tend to be quite serious. Scheduling breaks, vacations, and play in their calendars will help them to remember why they are working so hard in the first place.

Wood and Earth

Synergistic Qualities

- Wood finds Earth's compassion and loyalty endearing.
- Wood appreciates an Earth's tenderness and being reminded to stop, rest and take care of themselves.
- Earth is enamored by a Wood's structure, drive and fortitude to keep going even under extreme pressures.
- Earth is motivated by Wood and wants to muster the same energy to get behind their intentions.

Points of Friction

- Earth can feel threatened and view themselves as less than when comparing themselves to Wood.
- Wood can become frustrated with an Earth's tendency to resist change and seek comfort over excellence.
- Wood can perceive Earth as lazy when unwilling to push through and keep going. They can already envision the end result; why can't an Earth just get on board?
- Earth gets exhausted when a Wood becomes inflexible to other viewpoints or is unwilling to meet in the middle.

Supportive Energetic

Metal: Through appreciation, presence, and gratitude for what they have right now (along with what is possible if they come together), these types can better support each other's innate skills and move forward in a unified direction.

Earth and Water

Synergistic Qualities

- Both types can be themselves around each other. There is no need for masks or pretending things are something they're not.
- Earth can promote harmony through caretaking and reminding a Water to take care of their body through self-care practices.
- Earth can be a supportive center to come home to after Water returns from time off by themselves.
- Water assists Earth to dream and open their horizons to greater possibilities beyond what they can see or touch.
- Water can support Earth to connect with their intuition, take their time when making decisions, and create devotional practices to connect to the Divine.

Points of Friction

- Their comfort with each other can easily allow this couple to slide into complacency, where no growth or transformation happens and the objectives of the relationship become muddied.
- Earth can enable Water's indecisiveness by prioritizing harmony over constructive support, which can cause Water to doubt their intuition.
- Water's fear can paralyze an Earth and exacerbate their anxiety and worries, which can result in both feeling overly negative and depressed.

Supportive Energetic

Wood: Its capacity for visioning and strategy is helpful to motivate both Earth and Water to move ahead with their dreams and ideas, so each individual grows, evolves and transforms into their best selves.

Paired Relationships: Like Attracting Like

Paired relationships, where both individuals have the same dominant Element, can be a bit tricky. For some partnerships, they work very well, and for others, it's just too much of a good thing. This is because when two people are alike everything is mirrored and illuminated, both the gifts along with the insecurities and areas for growth. It's been my experience that for these relationships to thrive, strong communication skills are necessary to navigate the more challenging aspects of the relationship. Also both individuals must be willing to spend time apart from one another and to accept the supportive qualities of an outside energetic – either by supporting and reconciling each individual's secondary Element's core requirements or by seeking supportive friends or even counselors that offer an outside perspective.

Water and Water

Synergistic Qualities
- Both enjoy deep philosophical discussions and exchanging wisdom and ideas.
- Both are free to be themselves in their own authentic expression.
- They enjoy time away from each other to do their own thinking and adventuring.

Points of Friction
- There is a tendency for not a lot to get done.
- For Waters, to know is enough, and neither person may feel called to move things past the idea stage.
- With no action a melancholy or hopelessness can prevail.
- Fear can paralyze the relationship.

Supportive Energetic
Metal: It resonates with its slow flow, but it can also detach and pull Waters back on track by connecting their ideas to purpose, so they can begin moving forward to meet an objective.

Wood and Wood

Synergistic Qualities
- There is a productive, goal-oriented, forward-moving direction.
- Mountains are moved; obstacles are overcome; and empires are created.
- A deep respect is formed through witnessing each other go after their dreams and do what's necessary to achieve them.

Points of Friction

- A butting of heads can occur when both individuals want to lead and expect the other to follow.
- Both individuals may think they're right and be unwilling to acknowledge the opposing thought or direction.
- It's all work and conquer, no play, creativity or vacations. Materialism and excess can be idolized in place of life experience and something deeper.

Supportive Energetic

Water: Big-picture thinking can help bring Woods back to the source of their creativity and see what all their work and effort is for.

Fire and Fire

Synergistic Qualities

- Fun, play and pleasure are prioritized.
- Passion makes for an exciting relationship.
- They are social butterflies, the life of the party, and able to freely mingle with anyone.
- They have a wealth of connections with which to collaborate.

Points of Friction

- They don't always want to share the stage and spotlight with the other person, which can result in competition and contempt for each other.
- In always living for the moment, daily tasks and business may go unattended – over time, this will create anxiety and overwhelm.
- Drama is always a possibility, given high levels of emotional instability.

- There's a possibility to burn each other out – always riding the high and never coming down to go inward and consolidate their resources and vitality.

Supportive Energetic

Wood: Supportive, no-nonsense sarcasm can be the healthy dose of reality Fires need to slow down and ensure that work gets done. Momentum toward something more sustainable can be created while still having fun.

Earth and Earth

Synergistic Qualities

- These relationships are founded on supportive, nurturing, unconditional love for each other.
- Comfortable in the presence of one another, Earths accept each other as they are in this moment.
- Family and togetherness are prioritized.

Points of Friction

- These relationships can get complacent, with each individual avoiding things outside of their container of comfort.
- Feeling trapped by loyalty to certain roles and expectations will make Earths feel guilty and apathetic about their growth and development.
- Worry and anxiety can be heightened if both are stuck in their heads and unable to create resolution.

Supportive Energetic

Fire: This energetic infuses the relationship with play and invites them to try something new that may be outside of their comfort zone. At the same time, Fire provides a comforting warmth that is respectful of the relationship's foundations while also giving a gentle push to catalyze change and evolution.

Metal and Metal

Synergistic Qualities
- The relationship is based on excellence, intelligence, integrity and respect.
- Both individuals will recognize and acknowledge each other's expertise and skill.
- Often well read and highly educated, these individuals will be able to converse on topics of mutual interest.
- They can be in each other's company without engagement, and they might prefer it that way.

Points of Friction
- Life can easily get overly serious and lack spontaneity and fun.
- Given tendencies to be distant, detached and sometimes cold, the relationship can be void of warmth.
- Their self-reliance can result in them never checking in with each other and ultimately growing apart.

Supportive Energetic

Earth: This energetic can help Metals bridge the gap between them and to lighten up. It also brings a gentle joy to inspire connection and foster warmth, play and intimacy.

Community: We're Never Meant to Do This Alone

A Fire knows that life is better when we are surrounded by people we love. Being in a company of like-minded people who have similar interests and goals can facilitate an acceleration of thought, ideas and action that would take so much longer if each person were trying to figure it out for themselves.

Community and collaboration are essential to our well-being. On multiple levels, they support us in creating a life that we love. The road to self-discovery is an intimate and personal one, but it is made so much easier when we have others to support us and cheer us on. A supportive circle can help bridge the gap when we are struggling to believe our innate gifts and wisdom. Community and friendships are the shoulder we lean on when things get sticky or we feel like we're going backward instead of forward.

Being connected and in collaboration with others is a way to engage with the core requirements of Fire and can serve as a reminder that you are loved. They also affirm that it's safe to be seen and to stand out from the crowd to go after your dreams and desires. The other benefit of collaboration comes when there is synergy within a group. This energy is potent and can exponentiate the results and impact of the intended goal. Think tanks, supportive circles, and masterminds are examples of how individuals have chosen to come together to create change. Fire is a catalyst for transformation, and when you have multiple people joining together to put their collective energy toward an intention, big things are possible.

Even the more introverted yin Elements of Metal and Water can benefit from being in the presence of others. These interactions reaffirm that they don't have to do it all themselves. However, they may find it necessary to create boundaries for their participation. They may also need to assess how best to use their particular skill set and plan adequate time to do their part. This isn't so much an issue for Wood and Fire types. Fires are stoked to be surrounded by people working toward a cause. And if a Wood can see the potential for growth and harness their energy toward a vision, they are more than happy to lend a hand. An Earth meanwhile holds the container for everyone to come together and is often working behind the scenes at least energetically, creating harmony among the different personalities.

If you're feeling called to experience greater community or collaboration, trust your intuition and begin the process of finding your people. It may be as easy as reaching out to your Fire friend and sharing with them your desire for greater connection. They typically know a lot of people and have a knack for making friends wherever they go. They just might know exactly who you are meant to connect with, if it's not them themselves. If that isn't available to you, you may want to use social media platforms to search out groups focused on a particular interest you have, or even better, take a class in real life on a topic or activity that interests you. Get out of your house and sign up for something that you've always wanted to do; it's very likely that you will meet others who are seeking community just as you are.

Writing Prompts

What communities do I currently participate in?

How do I feel seen and supported within these communities?

Are there other opportunities for me to engage in community to be further supported or collaborate toward a common goal?

Play: Allowing Your Inner Child to Lead the Way

All work and no play make for a very dull flame. It's a silly little saying, but one I often use with my Fire clients when they are feeling a little out of sorts. If they've lost their spark, it's likely because they haven't taken the time to play or be spontaneous. Whether you're a Fire or not, every single one of us needs to play on a daily basis to continually stoke our inner flame of joy and desire.

Too often we fall victim to conditioning from childhood that trains us to believe play, much like rest, happens when work is complete. The problem is our work is no longer cleaning our bedroom or finishing that 45 minutes of homework. Instead, when one project or task is complete, there are ten more waiting for our attention. This is why it's so important that we reframe play and reprioritize it in our life even when there is still so much to do.

Play serves us in a multitude of ways. It allows us to connect to our bodies and remember that we are more than just a talking head. We all benefit and are energized from having the blood flowing and getting out from behind our desks or screens. Play inspires joy and reconnects us to our child-like spirit, the one that could play for hours until we were called in for dinner. Through play, we remember that we are free to create a reality all our own, one that excites us and is inspired by our heart's desires. Not only that but joy, laughter and play are contagious. I dare you to smile at someone; notice that they will inevitably begin to smile back at you. If you have the privilege to be near little ones, notice how when they laugh, you can't help but laugh with them, until you both collapse in full-body giggles of joy. Play brings you into the present, and perhaps paradoxically, it actually improves productivity. It fosters innovation and allows for the release of some of the pressure you may be experiencing as you try to buckle down and finish your agenda.

To make it simple and easy to implement in your day, I would invite you to make a list of activities that you enjoy – you may even want to think back to what you did as a child to gain greater inspiration – and then begin to schedule them in your calendar. You may find that you want to weave them into your daily agenda. For example, perhaps you want to schedule a dance break after you complete so many tasks or after each hour spent working. Partake in a lunchtime activity; head to the gym to play intramural sports or challenge yourself to run like the wind. Gather some friends or co-workers for a game, puzzle or activity after work. The possibilities are endless, and the payoffs are huge. Let your inner child lead the way.

Writing Prompts

What activities or games did I most love to do as a child?

When I think back to the whimsical activities of my childhood, when I had freedom to do what I wanted, what did play feel like in my body?

Make a list of at least 20 activities that you could try to inspire more play and fun in your life.

Celebration: Break Out the Good Dishes and Pop Open the Bubbles

When was the last time you celebrated something? Was it a huge milestone like an anniversary or birthday? Or did you celebrate something smaller, such as a win at work that made you feel proud of yourself? Much like play, celebration is something that most of us put off, usually reserving it for big things like a 40th or 50th birthday. We never celebrate 37 or 42 the same way, when really they are just as extraordinary. The same can be said for anniversaries. Nine years isn't as big a deal as 10 years. Forget 18 – who cares until you've made it to 20 or 25? REALLY?

We uphold odd rules about when we are allowed to revel in our accomplishments. The time has come to be a little more audacious and free as we share our wins, both big and small, with those we love. We actually need to allow ourselves to celebrate regularly, even daily if possible, because it's important to let off steam, laugh, expand our heart, and share our light with everyone in our circle of influence and beyond. If we don't take these opportunities, eventually things get a little messy and we burn out, having never taken the time to savor and honor ourselves.

Fire offers us the opportunity to engage with our joy and celebrate our life as it is, not waiting for one day when it looks how you'd like it to be. Pop the bubbly after you have that really difficult conversation with your boss. Use your fancy china and crystal just because. Dance your heart out when you've finished a task. I'm not even exaggerating when I tell you that after almost every section of this book – basically every 800 words or so – I would turn on the music and dance, or take Lily, our dog, out for a walk to recognize that I had crossed another threshold toward bringing this whole thing to completion.

Fire types, I know you have no issue thinking of ways to celebrate. However, for those types who aren't used to celebrating much, you may wish to take a closer look at your Alchemy to draw inspiration for what type of celebration supports your constitution and its core requirements. As an Earth, I get excited at the idea of hosting a huge dinner for friends, lighting way too many candles, cooking way too much food, serving wine, using the good china, having an exceptional playlist going in the background, creating ambience, and having deep conversations well into the night. Hosting gives me great joy and a ton of satisfaction, and it allows me to connect to people I adore. We all need more spontaneity, connection, and intimacy in our lives, and even if you're not accustomed to being the center of attention, it can feel really good every now and then to be seen, heard, understood and celebrated for all your amazing contributions to your work, family and circle of influence.

Writing Prompts

When was the last time that I celebrated me?

What is one thing that I could celebrate about myself today?

What activity, ritual or event can I do to honor an accomplishment?

Write out all the different ways that you can engage in celebration both big and small to assist you in regularly celebrating who you are and all that you do.

Philanthropy: Service and Legacy to Move from Me to We

When you have an open, loving heart and the tools to ensure that your core requirements are met, you may be ready to use your energy, compassion, and unconditional love to broaden your circle of influence and lift others up with you. When we have reconnected all the pieces of ourselves and are fully embodied, there is a ripple effect, which allows our influence and focus to widen beyond just ourselves.

It may seem slightly counterintuitive but for this to occur, you have to start with you. At the heart of any philanthropy or service that you may feel compelled to offer is your essence. You have a responsibility to yourself to ensure that what you wish to give and share is aligned with your heart and soul. The energetics of gifting must always be clean and pure of heart. You will feel it when they're not. If your offer is begrudging, obligatory, in service of your ego, conditional, or in exchange for favors or privileges, the organization may still greatly benefit from your donation of time or funds, but the impact will be dimmed by your lack of intention. I strongly believe that what we do with integrity carries immense energy that strengthens its impact and legacy, especially to the person or organization that is on the receiving end of your love and support.

A lot of us can get a bit stuck when we think of philanthropy; we aren't all billionaires with access to unlimited funds. But it can be as simple as asking yourself, what do I feel good to give? Philanthropy isn't about overextending yourself or sharing something you don't want to share. It can be anything you wish to give – money, time, or nurturing, to name some examples. This is actually a perfect place to explore your Alchemy and grant yourself permission to share and perform acts of service that are unique expressions of your heart. They don't have to look like anyone else's acts of service.

For some, it may still be donating to a favorite charity. For others, giving may lead to new and exciting opportunities. Do you want to meet new people and make new friendships? Do you wish to share your expertise in your industry with those just starting out, so they may skip over some of the harder lessons you had to learn in the beginning? Do you want to dust off your musical talents and perform at your local senior center? Read to young children at the library? Perhaps you feel compelled to honor your creativity and make something with your hands that will be given to someone who will be honored that so much care and attention was put into a gift especially for them.

For this area, I have intentionally avoided providing examples of how Element types tend to interact with acts of service. I prefer not to confuse or put barriers around what your relationship to philanthropy can be. Let your heart lead you toward acts of service that reflect your unique expression of love. There is nothing more valuable than when the soul guides us toward love. As each of us chooses and engages in authentic offerings of our love, we create a legacy and impact that extend far beyond our knowing. We transcend our individual humanity, needs, and desires – and become something far greater, a force that can change the world.

Writing Prompts

What is in my heart to give as an act of love and service?

How does my Alchemy support me in this act of love and service?

Protectors: Asserting Boundaries for Authentic Expression

At times Fire can be reckless and all consuming. It can burn us. For this reason, it is important to construct and assert boundaries so that we can remain open to its warmth, and the experiences it makes available to us, while protecting ourselves from being hurt.

I would like to point out that all but one of the Elements is associated with two paired organs in Chinese medicine. The outlier is Fire, which has four: the heart, the pericardium, the small intestine and the triple burner (an organ unique to Chinese medicine), all of which serve as the heart's protectors. This is in part because the heart wants to be open, loving and vulnerable at all times, except that this isn't always in its best interest. The other three organs serve to support the heart (considered the monarch of the body) by creating boundaries and differing levels for discernment to ensure that the heart remains sovereign, protected from being taken advantage of and in integrity with your soul's authentic expression.

As you further support your inner Fire's expression in the world – building connection, community and philanthropy – you have a responsibility to yourself to be in right relationship with the Fire Element and its areas of governance, no matter your Alchemy and your core requirements. This provides you with a power source that fuels your commitment and willingness to give. Every other being you meet has that same responsibility, even if they are completely unaware of it. Appropriate boundaries protect you and your heart from others treating you badly or leading you down a slippery slope to rationalizing someone's bad behavior. They empower you to share less of yourself, cut ties or hold someone at arm's length or lovingly call them out on their stuff when required. Doing so doesn't mean that you don't care for the other person deeply; you're simply honoring your own self agency first and foremost.

The truth is you should never feel compelled to share beyond what feels right and comfortable. Trust your inner knowing; it will keep you safe and ensure that your autonomy is respected. In some safe and loving relationships, the walls and boundaries that we create can be almost permeable; your love can burn bright and there is reciprocal trust. Then there may be relationships where you have small but necessary boundaries in place; they may be as simple as office hours to reflect your availability or putting your work notifications on silent during family dinner. There will also be relationships where you need to protect yourself with a 10-foot wall and a moat. On the outside, all these relationships look different, but by enacting these boundaries, you are showing the same capacity for love and compassion. Most importantly, you are putting yourself in a position to have healthy and respectful relationships.

You get to create and enact the protections you need at any given moment, in any relationship or act of service. You may find that these protections shift and change as greater trust and love are generated. Alternatively, if you feel that a stronger enforcement needs to be put in place, trust yourself. Creating or upholding a boundary is never something that you need to apologize for or explain away. By doing your own inner work, you have the opportunity to constantly navigate and reassess your relationships and decide the level of vulnerability that is appropriate for each.

Writing Prompts

In past or current relationships when have I let down my boundaries prematurely and been hurt?

In past relationships, what boundaries were helpful in upholding my integrity and the relationship's integrity?

What boundaries are helpful in my current relationships – whether they are romantic, working, friendship, or family?

A *Love Letter* to Your Inner Fire

You, my love, are meant to be seen, felt, heard, and celebrated. There's a reason why you are able to command a crowd and tantalize them with your brilliance. You are an inspiration, period. Every single person who has the opportunity to experience your warmth, wit and affection is so lucky. Don't ever forget this. In the moments where doubt creeps in, fall back on your circle and let them tend to your flame so that you can continue to show up in the world as you're meant to.

Remember, you step to the beat of your own heart. If you're feeling out of sync and burned out, it's because you've been trying to stay in tune with a beat that is not your own. Trust yourself and your own way. Play, pleasure and fun will always guide you back. So, take a nap, dance, do something that makes no sense, and whenever possible laugh until your belly hurts so that you can feel the sparkle return to your eyes. It is safe to go bigger and burn brighter; the world needs your light.

XO

Fire

Chapter 14

Your Next Steady Step

Exhale, and take a moment to think back on this journey. From taking the quiz, to that first rush of recognition when you read the description of your dominant Element type. Think about which self-inquiry questions most resonated with you. At the beginning of this journey, I reminded you that you are already whole. Now, having learned about how the 5 Element energetics culminate to inform your whole self and the life you live, do you feel more in touch with your innate wholeness?

I've noticed a funny thing with my clients who have actively engaged with their 5 Element Alchemy; they can't un-know it. Language and ideas that at first felt foreign and perhaps awkward to them end up reshaping their lens of perception. By the end of our sessions together, they confidently and lovingly reference the Elements and their energetics in the context of themselves and others, their relationships, their work, and their everyday lives. The 5 Elements allow them to weave together seemingly random events or quirks about themselves and those they love. Suddenly, it becomes clear that these things do fit together; they make sense. And where there was previously confusion, sadness or a tendency toward confrontation, a grounded peacefulness arises to help soften edges and bring peace and happiness.

The journey of self-discovery never ends. It merely deepens. This medicine will forever support you from this day forward if you let it. Your Alchemy and the 5 Elements can provide the compass that orients you back to your soul. The writing prompts provided in each of the chapters can provide you with valuable insights to amplify the whispers of your heart or inspire you to take empowered action. Come back to them as often as you need to. Each time you do, you will find a deeper level of awareness and healing, and confirmation that your soul is waiting to guide you to your next steps, into greater realms of influence and impact.

The more you lean into your Alchemy, the stronger your connection to it will become. Each Element will support you as you navigate decisions, make leaps of faith, and choose love over fear. Surrender to their medicine so that they may activate your potential and provide you evidence that it's safe to trust the steady steps that appear before you in the pursuit of creating a life that you love.

Allowing for Shifts

In the beginning of this book, I invited you to learn your Alchemy by way of a quiz. You then proceeded to develop a deeper understanding of it by reading about the different Element types. I hope the descriptions related to your dominant Element(s) resonated for you. More often than not, this is what happens. However, if this isn't what happened for you, there may be a good reason.

For some individuals, it is only after engaging with the different Element types that they realize that while on the surface they appear to be a certain Element type, they are in fact another. This can occur when they have constructed an elaborate and refined system of coping mechanisms to support a particular area of life at a particular time. Way back in the first chapter, we discussed how this happens with mothers of young children who often cultivate more Earth in their chart to allow them to be available to the needs of their child, releasing other energetics in order to create that space. These shifts can be useful, but they can persist past the point of usefulness and end up overriding and covering up their innate expression. At times, an entire identity can be created to continue to drive a narrative that has been developed due to outside influences. However, with a few shifts in perspective, this can fall away to allow one's true nature and tendencies to arise. It's as if a veil is lifted and their true Elemental potential is revealed.

Because the Elements aren't fixed, like some of the other personality typing systems, as we convene with their inner landscape, our true expression begins to make its way to the light, ready to support us in a way that we have yet to experience.

If you're feeling like there is something more to uncover here, I invite you to take the quiz again. Notice if any of your answers have changed. Are there qualities about yourself that at first you discounted or didn't recognize that are now fully embodied and ready to support you on this next step of your journey? In time you won't need the quiz to qualify you as one Element or another, because you will be able to access all of them within yourself and know which energetic you require for support and call it forward. But in the first few months of working with this medicine, the quiz can provide clarity and direction to help you engage with this medicine in a meaningful way that supports your transformation to the most authentic you.

One Element that is almost universally strengthened through this process of reflection is the Fire Element, as it must be intentionally tended. It's common, even for Fire types, to forget to tend to our flame as we encounter life stressors and hardships such as family issues, bills, and deadlines. When we're merely surviving and putting one foot in front of the other, it's easy to shove our desires and need for play and celebration to the side to pick up when times are better. Except, all too often, by that point the flame has fizzled so much that it can be difficult to remember what it's like to have a fully activated inner Fire. If this feels true to you, know that it can come back in a big way if you're willing to put your intention there.

One of my most memorable client stories was witnessing the Fire Element be reignited. When we first started working together, this client had a huge concentration of Metal, her secondary was Earth, with little representation in the other three Elements. At the time, she was out of work and her marriage had devolved to the point that they were roommates keeping a household running. She had resigned herself to believing that this would be okay. Through inquiry and a willingness to navigate the sensitive areas of her life with deep compassion, she found an inner embodiment of Fire begin to emerge. This allowed her to have the difficult conversations that resulted in the completion of a marriage that was no longer working for her or her spouse and nurturing her flame by engaging with her desires. Work opportunities that excited her began to emerge along with love and passion with a new romantic partner who sees and supports her, allowing her to receive love that felt unimaginable before.

All this to say, if there is any part of the Elements and their life's governance that you think isn't yours to experience, think again. Through self-discovery and listening to your heart, you will cultivate opportunities in the areas of each and every one of the Elements to nurture you in creating a life in alignment with your heart and soul.

Navigating Uncertainty

No matter how much we think we have our life together, we will still experience moments of uncertainty, doubt and fear every now and again. We cannot bubble wrap our lives to ensure that we won't experience pain or hardship, as this would only prevent us from living to our fullest capacity and potential.

The good news is that with the 5 Elements you have solid tools and strategies to turn to when you encounter such moments. You needn't look further than your Alchemy's core requirements. Let's be honest. Your core requirements aren't going anywhere. They're going to try to be met in these moments anyways, so we may as well consciously bring them to the forefront and consider whether an opportunity or relationship is satisfying them and in what way. That way, they can help guide your decisions and actions in a way that protects both your integrity and autonomy.

Each time that you come back to your own needs, you help to confirm and affirm that you know what is best for you. That you have the answers you seek. Outward sources can only offer suggestions from the lens of their Alchemy and experience. While there may be some helpful pearls of wisdom for you to consider, they must always be seen and interpreted through your own lens, your Alchemy and your core requirements. Let your core requirements provide you the necessary questions that require answers before you jump or stay the course. These questions have powerful and revolutionary potential, as they will provide you a framework that makes it okay to opt out of society's conventions and instead create and live the life you dream of, not the one that you've been taught to settle for.

This may lead to huge shifts in your life that appear to fall out of the sky. Outsiders who aren't privy to the full capacity of your inner knowing may believe you've done a complete 180 and feel compelled to question your sanity. This is what happened to a Fire/Water client of mine who chose to move her whole life to another city after having spent only a few weeks' vacation there. When she came to me, she was feeling isolated in her life, unable to make meaningful connections. On a whim, in Fire fashion, she picked a small town near the water to vacation and fell in love. Within days she met like-minded individuals that she could meet for tea on the daily, business owners that she felt proud to support, and peace from being near the water, which soothed her soul like only it can. Upon returning home, she checked in with her core requirements and talked it over with her husband, ensuring that his Alchemy's core requirements would also be supported. Then they made the decision. They were moving across the country to live in the quaint little town that made her heart dance, where her Fire could be celebrated. The universe backed her up by lining up the most serendipitous events like her husband getting a job offer that was so much more fulfilling than the one he previously had and finding the perfect property to buy. Everything arrived with divine timing to make each next step welcomed with grace.

Another possibility is that your awareness will broaden so that you notice that there is a world of support available to give you a helping hand. Our culture considers self-reliance a virtue, but too often it is misconstrued and just results in people isolating themselves and being unwilling to ask for help. A Water client of mine found herself overwhelmed, as though the world was swallowing her whole. When she finally shared what was really going on in her life to a close circle of people, you could feel the dam break open. She didn't have to do it all on her own; in fact, she had to be willing not to. And she could still navigate her needs for safety, security and freedom while allowing others to assist and support her. This new mindset led to a new job that paid her well for her skills and helped to provide a generous cushion so that she could still dream of bigger possibilities. Travel landed in her lap that expanded her horizons even more. All because she made the brave choice to surrender to the support that was available to her all along and allow her core requirements to be reconciled in a whole new way.

Keep your requirements close and check in with them often. Notice how reconciling them in the most kind and compassionate way brings about transformation that is fueled by ease instead of struggle. Allow yourself to ask, how can these needs be met more easily and with greater grace?

Return to Compassion

The road to healing often has many bumps and unexpected turns. This can create a tendency to be incredibly hard on ourselves, judging or blaming ourselves for all the times when we turned our back on our heart and the calling of our soul, or made a decision that we thought would work out but didn't. I fully believe that each of us does the best that we can with what we have at any given moment.

It's easy to look back and live in the hypotheticals, the could've, would've and should've's, especially knowing what we know now. It's tempting to relive those moments and fantasize about possibilities, except it really doesn't matter. There is no value in playing out a timeline that doesn't exist. Instead, what we need is compassion, for our younger selves and the circumstances that culminated to create our current reality.

If you really must reminisce, do so through the heart-centered lens of compassion. Notice how your Alchemy and the unconscious reconciling of your core requirements helped get you through, even if you didn't know it at the time. Acknowledge your resiliency and the persistence that allowed you to rise above your challenges and still meet so many of your goals with whatever tools you had at your disposal. You are incredible; you were then, and you are now. And your future self, which now has a whole new arsenal of supports to call upon to create impact and change in your life and the lives of others, will be too.

Allow self-compassion to be a trusty travel companion that you can defer to whenever self-doubt and criticisms start to speak louder than your heart; let it help lead you back to your brilliance.

Permission to Be Yourself

You are the authority on you. Stand proud and embrace everything that you are. Do not apologize for any of it, ever.

Life is too short to be anyone other than who you are meant to be. Having witnessed both the struggle and the miracle of souls choosing life as a fertility acupuncturist, I can affirm that each and every one of us chose to say yes to the light, and we are all capable and meant to experience and do miraculous things in this world.

Allow this moment to be the one where you choose to go for it: the dream, the job, the love, the adventure, or perhaps all of them. DO IT! Having uncovered and honored your Alchemy, you can trust that the Elements will support you. Wherever you decide to jump, you will land exactly where you're supposed to.

You do not need to wait for validation or approval from others. You get to trust your inner compass and the knowing that has been waiting all this time for you to access. It doesn't matter if your path looks different from those of everyone else you know. That's the point. We each have a unique expression that requires our attention and devotion to manifest into form. You can trust your pace; there is a rhythm of creativity and implementation that will guide you through your own personal ebb and flow. It knows when to slow down or come to a stop, and it will kick into high gear when you're ready, taking you far in no time at all.

Allow the Element type descriptions to provide you with reminders of what you already know to be true. Revisit them as often as you need to, each time with a beginner's mind, and notice what you didn't pick up on before. There may be a new layer that is ready to reveal itself to you that will provide the necessary information to level up your life in ways that you could never imagine. Take what feels aligned in this moment and leave what doesn't; choose the practices and areas of your life that feel most supportive to your current circumstance and see where they take you. When you feel as though things need to be reorganized, trust that something new will emerge to support your liberation and next steps in a way that feels good to your soul.

Perhaps unbeknownst to you, when you first picked up this book, you were initiated into the deep dive of self-discovery to come home to your soul to allow your profound wisdom to come forward. You showed up, you did the work, and if you haven't already taken the time to celebrate yourself for answering the call, do it now. I want to remind you that you are enough, you are worthy, you are safe, you are powerful, you are loved, and you are whole. No matter where life takes you next, these innate truths can never be diminished.

Revel in your accomplishments and share your light. I would be so honored if you would share it with me using #5ElementAlchemy or tag me in your social media posts so that I can raise my glass and witness the blossoming of your soul. You are only going to grow and flourish to even greater heights and impact as you continue to express your Alchemy out in the world.

XO
Ashley

Acknowledgments

I would first like to acknowledge my grandmother Eileen Elliott, the catalyst to me finding a profession and field of medicine that I love and the eventual writing of this book. In 2001, she fell ill, and Western allopathic medicine was unable to figure out why she was enduring so much pain. This led my family to seek other forms of treatment including acupuncture and Chinese medicine.

Little did I know that her and my destinies were interwoven. As I watched her vitality and giggle return with each treatment, I fell in love with the medicine. The acupuncturist who worked with her for many months, Dr. Jagdeep Johal, became my first mentor and introduced me to the world of transformational healing, the importance of honoring our emotions, and the 5 Elements. Thank you, Jug, for taking the time all those years ago. The serendipity of meeting you through my grandma helped align my life in accordance with my soul's truest expression.

Thank you to my husband, Sheldon, whose support, generosity and patience are unmatched. You deserve a medal; there's just no other way to say it. I love you. I am forever grateful that I get to travel through this life beside you.

Elijah, my sun, moon and stars. You granted me the gift of being your mother, and your arrival was my initiation to begin writing. I would never in a million years have considered myself a writer let alone an author. Thank you for helping uncover this truth. You inspire me every day to delve deeper into this medicine and come home to my soul so that I may rise to the opportunity of honoring your light.

My parents, Brenda and Doug Abbs, you have always encouraged me to go after what I want and to dream bigger. Thank you for your guidance, unconditional love, and enduring enthusiasm for what sparks my imagination.

To my mentor Lorie Dechar, this project has been a long time coming. I am so grateful for our private conversations, your sage advice and friendship. Your work inspires me to journey further inward, listen to my soul and trust myself. Your words and teachings have been vital to both my writing and how I show up in the treatment room with patients. Thank you for mentoring and holding space for me to find my voice so that I may speak up to share my heart in the wider world.

Thank you to Randine Anderson Lewis, I feel so very lucky to have been given the opportunity to learn with you. Your teachings have not only helped me become skilled in the realm of fertility and acupuncture but I hear your voice continually in my head, inviting me to seek more ways to live this medicine in my everyday life.

There would be no book without the 20 years of friendship and guidance of my editor, Kathryn Willms. You helped me transform a tentative first draft into something that I am proud of. I am a better writer as a result of your advice, expertise and positivity. Who would ever have thought that you editing my university papers all those years ago would bring us here. I am in awe of how the serendipity of a random dorm placement culminated in us collaborating on this project and hopefully many more.

Nick Suche and his team at Talon x, for your graphics work and website design. You guys always make my visions 100x better than my original conception.

Angela Hammersmith of Hammersmith Designs, for the stunningly beautiful book cover.

And to my clients: This book is a love letter to you. Thank you for sharing often the most intimate details of your lives with me. Sitting beside you during our sessions, listening to the incredible sorrow, frustration and also moments of ecstatic joy as your desires manifest into form helped inspire this book. It is because of you that others may have the opportunity to inquire within and come into greater alignment with who they are, so that they too can create a life they love. Thank you for entrusting me with your healing journeys.

About the Author

Ashley Abbs B.A. Dr.Ac. Dip.TCM. FABORM.

Dr. Ashley Abbs is a writer, acupuncturist, spiritual embodiment mentor and the owner of TerraSana Health and Wellness Centre.

She graduated from the University of Calgary with a bachelor's degree in psychology and completed her acupuncture studies at the Alberta College of Acupuncture and Traditional Chinese Medicine (ACATCM) graduating as a doctor of acupuncture with an additional diploma in Traditional Chinese Medicine. She is also a fellow of the American Board of Oriental Reproductive Medicine (ABORM).

Drawing on her clinical experience and the medicine of the 5 Elements, when not in her private acupuncture practice, Ashley leads online courses and mentorships encouraging individuals to embrace their innate gifts, activate their intuition and embody their wholeness to create a life of love & legacy. She currently lives in her home city of Calgary, Alberta, Canada, with her husband Sheldon and son Elijah.

You can visit her online at www.ashleyabbs.com, or follow her on Instagram @ashleyabbs and on Facebook @drashleyabbs.

#5elementalchemy

Manufactured by Amazon.ca
Bolton, ON